PLANNING FOR HOSPITAL EXPANSION AND REMODELING

PLANNING FOR HOSPITAL EXPANSION AND REMODELING

By

DONALD C. CARNER

Executive Vice President
Memorial Hospital
Long Beach, California

With a Foreword by

Ray E. Brown, Director

Graduate Program in Hospital Administration
Duke University
Durham, North Carolina

CHARLES C THOMAS · PUBLISHER
Springfield · Illinois · U.S.A.

Published and Distributed Throughout the World by
CHARLES C THOMAS • PUBLISHER
BANNERSTONE HOUSE
301-327 East Lawrence Avenue, Springfield, Illinois, U.S.A.
NATCHEZ PLANTATION HOUSE
735 North Atlantic Boulevard, Fort Lauderdale, Florida, U.S.A.

With THOMAS BOOKS *careful attention is given to all details of manufacturing and design. It is the Publisher's desire to present books that are satisfactory as to their physical qualities and artistic possibilities and appropriate for their particular use.* THOMAS BOOKS *will be true to those laws of quality that assure a good name and good will.*

Printed in the United States of America
T-1

DEDICATION

This book is dedicated to the memory of Arthur G. Bachmeyer, M.D., physician, educator, administrator, author, preceptor and friend to untold numbers of practicing physicians and hospital executives.

FOREWORD

PLANNING for Hospital Expansion and Alteration does an excellent job of filling one of the important gaps in the hospital literature. Other books of this sort are sorely needed. The excellent manner with which it fills the particular gap to which it is addressed sharply identifies the need for this and other books and defines the approach and format they require.

The hospital is marked by its diversities. No other enterprise is involved with so many different activities nor charged with so many different purposes. The same can be said as regards the diversity of its affairs and the number of diverse interests concerned with its affairs. Said another way, the hospital must use many different means to satisfy many different ends. As regards hospital literature, this means many different things must be known by many different individuals and groups. For those who attempt to write about the hospital this also means they must in instances write differently about the same thing for different audiences.

In general, knowledge of what should be done about the hospital is not the same as the knowledge required to do it. It is somewhat the difference as between understanding the questions and knowing the answers. This difference dictates in many instances two sets of hospital literature — a body of knowledge about the questions and a body of knowledge about the answers.

Those responsible for answering the questions must have access to both bodies of knowledge but those responsible for asking for the answers can hardly be expected to be knowledgeable about more than the questions. The first group are the professionals and technologists who need the expertise associated with their particular special field. The second group is made up of hospital trustees and administrators, various public and private agency representatives which deal with the hospital, and various members of the community with which the hospital must seek consensus.

Since World War II there has been a steady development in the technical literature of the hospital. Most of the wide spectrum of technologies involved in hospital affairs and operations has been covered with manuals and monographs. The American Hospital Association has devoted substantial funds and energies to the development of this much needed material for use by the specialized doers. However, most of the technical material is beyond the ken and the span of time and interest of the question makers. Because of the lack of a literature usable by the generalists the specialists at times have been placed in the frustrating position of answering questions that no one was asking.

The topic of this book is a good example of the above situation. Much has been learned about the subject of hospital planning and the principles and methodologies required in determining need, facility layout, capital funding, etc., but no one would argue that the specialists in planning have been permitted to make their optimal contribution to hospital planning. Often the expertise of the specialists has not influenced the decision because the decisionmakers did not know what expertise was required. More often the expertise has been subordinated to other considerations because the decisionmakers did not understand what all needed to be considered and the priorities to be given to various considerations.

The value of this book is that it does examine and outline the variety of considerations that must go into the hospital's planning process. It will not enable the reader to become an expert in any of the aspects of hospital planning but it will enable him to carry on productive dialogues with the experts and alert him to the necessity of such dialogues.

RAY E. BROWN, *Director*
Graduate Program in Hospital Administration
Duke University
Durham, North Carolina

INTRODUCTION

NOT long ago a 76-year-old patient, near death, was rushed to a New York hospital by ambulance, suffering a complete heart block. His life was saved by the application of massive jolts of electricity from an external electronic stimulator, which helped maintain his heartbeat. It soon was evident that the patient's life depended on almost constant electrical stimulation of the heart.

The resident in surgery guided a cardiac catheter through a vein and into the patient's heart. The catheter contained an electrode, which then was connected to an electrical heart stimulator known as a pacemaker. With low voltage it was possible to control the patient's heartbeat. In addition, following the advice of the cardiologist, hospital attendants kept him on medicines that would prevent his blood from clotting.

Remarkable, isn't it? A 76-year-old man returned from the threshold of death, and his life maintained by a combination of electricity and chemicals. Yet, this isn't the whole story. After several months of care the doctors noted that the man's heart action had improved greatly. The pacemaker was disconnected and the treatment ended. The patient walked out of the hospital, a very happy man.

This patient's experience illustrates the recent, tremendous strides made in hospital care.

Because of these advances, more than twenty-eight and one-half million Americans are admitted to hospitals each year. One family in four will have a member hospitalized during the next twelve months.

Another measuring rod applied to hospitals to determine the extent of their role in modern society is the number of people employed. One out of every fifty persons working in America today is a hospital employee. Close to two million workers earn their living serving the ill in hospitals. More than a million people volunteer their services. Scores of thousands of students obtain an essential portion of their education in hospitals. More than 200,000 doctors devote an important segment of their time to direct patient care within hospitals.

This heavy concentration of patients, workers, and doctors effectively utilize plant and equipment valued at more than twenty billion dollars. Yet authorities agree that the nation is short tens of thousands of hospital beds and that more than a billion dollars is needed urgently just to rehabilitate existing hospital buildings.

George Bugbee, President, Health Information Foundation, has pointed out that in just fifty years the hospital changed its function from terminal care for the unfortunate individual without resources to a highly complex organization designed to bring together all the dramatic potentials and wonders of modern medical science.

"Few can envision a lifetime without helpful medical and hospital care, although not so long ago a man could take just pride in saying he never had been in a hospital in his life," said Mr. Bugbee.

While growing rapidly in scope of service to patients, in numbers of persons employed, volunteers, dollars invested, supplies consumed, students taught, and by any unit of measure, hospitals also have been the scene of significant and ever-expanding research in medicine and health. Thus it is that the hospital has become a basic element in American health and economy. Those who would serve their fellow man in the health field will find their paths intertwined closely with that of hospitals today, and undoubtedly more so in the future.

The underlying reason for the skyrocketing admission of patients to hospitals and the remarkable increase in scope of service and all that this calls for in personal effort, plant and equipment simply is the high value with which Americans regard each human life. As cures for cancer, heart disease, and other major causes of death are developed, they undoubtedly will be made available to patients through hospitals. Who in America would have it otherwise?

Sparked by the knowledge that, regardless of cost, even more lives must be saved, disease conquered, illness shortened and recovery made more complete, private enterprise and government are pouring an ever-increasing flow of dollars and effort in medical research. All of this can have but one effect: hospitals will continue to carry an ever-increasing degree of responsibility for the health of the people. The products of research become even more complex, requiring greater numbers of highly skilled and technically trained workers plus heavy dollar expenditures. For example, some cancer is responding to treatment afforded by multimillion-volt radiation. This requires a machine costing close to $150,000 plus specialized construction at an added expenditure of $35,000, must be maintained by highly skilled technicians and operated by doctors specializing in radiation therapy. Only a hospital could carry the responsibility for placing such equipment at the disposal of the patient and having it available for instant use twenty-four hours every day.

To keep pace with the demands placed upon hospitals, expansion and modernization must be stepped-up across the nation. Millions, even billions of dollars will be invested in this essential construction activity.

We hope that this book will serve as a guide to those charged with the responsibility for the effective utilization of these funds as they are placed to work in the public interest.

ACKNOWLEDGMENTS

S PECIAL appreciation is due to Motivation, Inc., *Hospitals,* and *Trustee* for their permission to draw extensively from some of my previous writings which first appeared in their publications. Chapter XIV is excerpted from "How to Develop a Successful Long Term Fund Program" by permission of Motivation, Inc. and *Trustee* magazine published by the American Hospital Association. Chapters VI and XVI are reprinted by permission of *Trustee* magazine and the American Hospital Association.

The illustrations are reproduced by permission of Eddie Hoff of Hollywood, photographer, Willens & Bertisch Co., Inc., of Los Angeles, project general contractor, and W. A. Lockett of Long Beach, the project architect.

Mr. Ted Krec, of Memorial Hospital of Long Beach, kindly reviewed and edited the material and Mrs. J. B. Parker, of the same institution, transformed badly cluttered pages of copy into a professional appearing manuscript which evoked editorial approval. However, had it not been for the sustained moral support from my wife, Hazel Kruse Carner, which began prior to the publication of my first article and continued for twenty years marked by innumerable rejection slips from magazine editors, I would have closed the typewriter long ago and given up any effort to write. For this continued encouragement I am everlastingly appreciative.

D. C. C.

CONTENTS

Page

Foreword vii

Introduction ix

Acknowledgments xiii

Chapter

I. OPPORTUNITY 3
    The Challenges 3
    Some Answers 5

II. CLASSIFICATIONS 11
    Ownership 11
    Size 14
    Teaching Hospitals 15
    Convalescent Hospitals and Nursing Homes 15

III. HOW HOSPITALS FUNCTION 17
    Essential Elements 17
    Common Goal 17
    Checks and Balances 18

IV. THE PLANNING AND EXPANSION TEAM 23
    Initiation of Expansion 23
    Building Committee 23
    Professional Advisers 24

V. TOTAL DESIGN FACTORS 27
    Better Facilities 27
    Utilization Higher—Lower Operating Costs 29
    Future Expansion 32

Chapter *Page*

VI. INTERIOR DESIGN 33

    Obtaining Professional Advice 34

    Guide to Selection 36

    Assignment Checklist 38

    Interior and Exterior Excellence 39

VII. MONEY-SAVING TIPS 40

VIII. PITFALLS 47

IX. EQUIPMENT 51

X. STAFFING 55

    Staffing Standards 55

    Quality Control 56

    Preopening Personnel 58

    Medical Staff 59

XI. TEST RUN 62

    Clean-up 62

    Receiving, Inspecting and Placing Equipment 62

    Break-in Period 63

    Employee Orientation 63

XII. PUBLIC ACCEPTANCE 65

    Golden Opportunity 65

    Stepladder to Success 66

    Information in Depth 67

XIII. FINANCING EXPANSION 70

    Need for Funds 70

    Sources 71

    Voluntary Fund Drives 73

    Hospital Bond Issues 75

    Lease Purchasing 76

Chapter   *Page*

        Bank Finance Mortgage Loans 77

        Insurance Company Mortgage Loans 77

        Mortgage Loan Underwriters 78

XIV. LONG TERM FUND DEVELOPMENT 80

        Gifts From Other Agencies 81

        An Associates Group 82

        Attracting Donor Dollars to Hospital Projects 84

XV. LONG RANGE PLANNING 86

        Avoidable Crises 86

        How to Plan 87

        Timing, Strategy, Tactics 89

XVI. TOMORROW'S HOSPITAL 90

        Hospitals in Transition 92

        Appendix: EXCERPTS FROM "GUIDELINES FOR INDIVIDUAL
        HEALTH FACILITY LONG RANGE PLANNING" 95

          General Trends Which Affect Community Needs ... 95

          Committee Organization and Operation for
            Individual Health Facilities 97

          Planning Procedures 98

      Index 107

PLANNING FOR HOSPITAL EXPANSION AND REMODELING

Chapter I

OPPORTUNITY

THE CHALLENGES

DOCTORS can't get beds for their patients—corridors are jammed, labs and x-ray departments are packed tightly with equipment, sick people are on stretchers parked in hallways while waiting to be seen, and the surgery schedule is impossible.

Patient rooms were built long before the day of the seven-foot, all-electric bed.

Bedside tables, overbed tables, chairs, suction equipment and dressers are stacked up so that furniture must be shifted to get a wheeled stretcher into the room to pick up a patient.

Outside, it is virtually impossible to park within a block of the hospital. The neighborhood has deteriorated so that nurses are afraid to walk to their cars at the late change of shifts.

Wings are added here and there in response to numerous crises so that floor levels vary from section to section. Walking distances seems interminable. Operating costs are high. No service seems to be related properly to the others.

Yet this is the building that scores, hundreds, and even thousands of lives are dependent upon every year. Fire Department officials cringe when they get an emergency call. A fire in the trash chute. Next it may be an overloaded electrical circuit buried deep in some forgotten, patched-over partition with fire racing through ceiling ducts and pipe chases. The odds against getting infants out of bassinets and patients in traction evacuated — almost nil.

Expansion and remodeling is long overdue. Action must be taken. Now! But this time it must be a complete overhaul, not just a piecemeal portion to meet the most serious crisis of the moment or to satisfy only the loudest voices.

The great majority of hospitals today are tremendously handicapped by having to occupy old, obsolete, overcrowded, worn-out structures. Many buildings in maximum use today were designed years ago and well before the advent of scientific medicine. Most great advances in scientific diagnostic and therapeutic equipment have taken place in the last twenty years: cine radiography, automated laboratory equipment, isotopology. These aids did not exist until recently. Today, valuable aids to diagnosis and therapy used to prolong life must be jammed into space already suffering from earlier cramming to accommodate a prior crisis.

All too often patients are admitted to unsafe structures. Even where the building is relatively secure, rooms were not designed to receive elaborate life-saving equipment needed at many bedsides. Electrical circuits were not wired to carry half the current load. Toilet facilities may be located some distance from the bedside. These facilities were planned in the days when the average length of stay was more than fourteen days, and when an obstetrician would not dream of discharging a mother short of ten days stay. These facilities are obsolete today.

Old high-ceiling structures with partitions made of clay building blocks firmly resist adaption to accommodate piped oxygen and suction. An electronic intercom between nurse and patient is difficult to install. Placing labor-saving pneumatic tubes and automatic unloading dumb waiter shafts is a virtual impossibility. If vertical transportation must be increased due to the steep rise in hospital traffic as activity moves upward at a rapid pace, planners are faced with an extremely serious problem.

Many hospitals have added pieces of structures here and there as best they could. Frequently this resulted in a hodge-podge of building that remains inadequate. While meeting the need of the moment, this does so at very heavy cost, both initially and for years to come.

Physical and occupational therapy, isotope equipment, coffee shops, gift shops, expanded laboratory, pressure breathing, x-ray and pharmacy services can augment hospital income significantly . . . provided space is adequate and well located. Full-size patient rooms and well-designed nursing units, along with properly planned food, linen, housekeeping and maintenance departments help reduce wasted hours of payroll time. Wide corridors with floors and walls covered with wear-resistant materials speed traffic and lower maintenance costs. The combination of added income achieved by servicing more patients with a broader range of services, coupled with lower operating costs achievable as a result of spacious, well-designed and well-equipped buildings can go a long way toward paying for the cost of remodeling and expansion.

SOME ANSWERS

What is needed? What combination of talent and circumstances is required to achieve for your hospital today that which has not been accomplished in the past? Can your hospital now be expanded and remodeled effectively?

Roadblocks need to be removed. That they can be has been demonstrated clearly by a number of leading hospitals. The answer is a firm "yes!"

Hospitals long have been underfinanced. Regardless of what price people pay for hospital care, they regard it as too high and offer complaints. Responding to this, trustees everywhere have held the rate structure down so low that income does not generate sufficient funds to permit normal expansion and remodeling, as is the case with most business enterprises. Capital also is very restricted from the viewpoint of most businesses. Only in the limited number of proprietary hospitals can a new issue of stock be sold to obtain capital for expansion.

Prospects of obtaining adequate capital for expansion and remodeling have improved remarkably in recent years. There are several reasons for this. Banks, insurance companies and hospital equipment and supply firms now will loan funds to a well-managed hospital. Even ten years ago it was most difficult to obtain borrowed funds from these sources.

Lending agencies, regardless of their composition, will insist that the hospital be managed well. Fortunately the quality of hospital management is on a definite up-grade, and for a sound reason. Thirty years ago the University of Chicago pioneered in the development of a graduate program within the framework of its School of Business to prepare competent people specially for the position of chief executive officer of a hospital. The success of this program encouraged the Kellog Foundation to aid in estalishing comparable courses in a number of universities following the close of World War II. Close to twenty graduate programs in hospital administration are producing annually almost 300 trained people for this highly specialized, very complex field of management. The influx of carefully selected, well-trained management personnel has supplemented effectively an existing supply of administrative leaders who earned their top-level executive posts by successfully passing through the school of experience. Today's hospitals are better managed than ever before; hence the new willingness of financial institutions to back hospitals with capital. One major roadblock to expansion and remodeling has been removed.

Closely related to improved management is the fact that a well-designed and equipped hospital can provide excellent patient care at lower costs than can its outmoded counterpart, the obsolete old hospital. Industry, serving hospitals, has developed successfully many effective time-saving devices which, if carefully incorporated in the expanded and remodeled hospital and carefully supervised by sound management, can reduce payroll hours and dollars markedly. As payroll may reach 70 per cent of operating costs, achieving a savings of 15 per cent in payroll time, may reduce total costs 10 per cent. This saving can help materially in financing major capital improvements. For example, a 100 bed hospital may have 250 employees and an annual payroll of $1,000,000. If a modern, excellently designed and equipped building is well managed, as much as $150,000 would be available annually to liquidate a $1,000,000 expansion loan.

An ideal hospital building with effective management will make another important contribution to capital financing for remodeling and expansion. More patients will want to use the better facilities. Doctors will admit more patients. The hospital will be able to function with a higher percentage of beds and related facilities in use, but without a proportional increase in operating costs. It used to be a rule of thumb that a hospital should not have more than 80 per cent occupancy, on the average for the year. Today leading hospitals base their annual budgets on year round occupancy factor of between 85 and 90 per cent occupancy. The increase in income from higher use without a proportionate increase in expense provides funds to retire loans needed for expansion and remodeling. A 5 per cent gain in occupancy in a 100 bed hospital could free $50,000 for debt service.

Another financial factor beginning to ease the bind is successful adaptation by hospitals of the long-term, low-pressure, fund-development concept perfected by colleges and universities. Until quite recently, when a hospital needed funds for expansion, its only hope was to bring in a professional fund-raising firm to guide an intensive campaign for contributions. Thousands of successful intensive hospital fund drives have raised untold millions of dollars for expansion . . . and will raise many more millions in the years to come. But the unfortunate fact is that to succeed, the hospital must be close to failure . . . the bed situation must be in a near crisis. Professional fund raisers, when called in, immediately search for the most pressing problems. Without being able to point to emergent needs, they may fail to obtain the level of response needed from donors if the campaign is to succeed. Counter to this, long-term, low-pressure, fund-development thrives on the basis of successful management and avoidance of the crisis. People give money, property and securities to the hospital on a life income or annuity contract in which they retain income for life from their gift. Such donors want a stable, well-managed organization handling their funds; not one governed by expediency and crisis. A representative group of hospitals has achieved considerable success in this relatively new field of endeavor. The door is open for most hospitals to obtain $100,000 a year and more through this activity.

Another ingredient in the successful hospital's expansion and remodeling program is found in the willingness of hospitals to call upon experts from outside the organization . . . consultants. Expert help is needed, especially in building design. Not many hospitals plan major expansion programs with enough frequency to stay fully abreast of changes that occur in design, in the use of building materials and in the furnishings field. Few community architects are called upon often enough to specialize in the complex business of designing hospitals. Hospital executives may have the competency to aid effectively in the design if they have a free hand. However, quite often it is essential to have an outside expert step in to keep a program in balance. One element or another of the hospital may try to gain an inordinate share of space and equipment. It is very difficult to handle this delicate situation without an independent, impartial, outside expert. Emotions may get tight and personality factors enter in, which could set the expansion and remodeling program back many years. Or an out-of-balance structure may result, which would handicap the hospital seriously for years ahead.

I recall a situation where the leading surgeon, a very competent, honest, ethical and well-intended man, insisted that a medium-sized community hospital without a medical education program should construct an overhead viewing gallery directly above each of four operating rooms. Each gallery would cost many thousands of dollars. Of greater importance, such galleries could not possibly be used with any frequency, and yet together they would block out eight beds on the floor above surgery . . . at a potential loss of income well in excess of $50,000 a year, while also denying admission of hundreds of patients to the hospital. The consultant was able to hold the viewing room construction down to one, which seemed reasonable enough as the hospital did have a school of nursing. Recently, even this single viewing room was eliminated and the space converted to a patient room. Closed-circuit TV is more effective than overhead viewing space.

Many hospitals now are calling upon management consulting firms to aid in the solution of perplexing daily operating problems as apart from questions that arise in building programs. One of the nation's leading management consulting firms reports that "institutional consulting," the section of the firm working with hospitals, colleges, etc., is growing at a vastly greater rate than the division devoted to industry and commerce. This 180 degree change in direction has taken place within a very few years.

Probably it is due to the fact that better qualified management is more fully aware of techniques developed in other fields which can help the hospital provide better care without wasting a penny from the patient's purse.

Happily today, hospitals in some areas, geographically and functionally speaking, are working more closely together to overcome the fact that even though they may be one of the largest employers in any community, they still are relatively small economic entities. Ninety Sourthern California hospitals formed the Commission for Administrative Services to Hospitals, a cooperative venture employing the talents of five industrial engineers to set work standards throughout the hospital in a concerted effort to lower costs without impairing quality. In two years, millions of dollars of payroll hours were saved. Aided by the alert Kellogg Foundation, the C.A.S.H. program spread to Northern California with equal success. Another Kellogg-sponsored group, Hospital Administrative Services, now has well over 1,200 hospitals across the nation exchanging vital operating statistics regarding employee productivity and other cost factors. Still another is Professional Activities Service. Again initially financed with Kellogg Foundation funds, now entirely self supporting, this is a group of hundreds of hospitals utilizing a computer located in Michigan to process and analyze statistics from medical records with the aim of improving the quality of professional care patients receive.

In summary, your hospital expansion and remodeling program *can* move forward today with greater expectation for full success than ever before. Many roadblocks have been removed. Necessary capital is more readily available. Management has been strengthened. The effective capacity of the hospital has been raised. New income-producing services will flourish. Better design and materials make possible lower operating costs. Outside experts are welcomed to aid in solving complex design and operating questions. Closer cooperation between hospitals helps overcome the inherent economic disadvantage of relatively small size.

However, expansion and remodeling is a major undertaking. A great deal of time, effort and money must be devoted to the project. Is it worth it?

From the patient's viewpoint, the answer can only be a resounding, "YES!" Certainly he wants greater safety, more comfort, extended diagnostic and therapeutic services, and every effort to save his health dollar.

Much of the burden will fall upon the physician; particularly upon the current leaders of the medical staff. Feathers will ruffle and toes will be stepped on. Contributions from the medical pocketbook may be required. Doctors can visualize being able to admit patients as their condition indicates, rather than as beds permit; ample operating suites, delivery rooms, and nurseries; better equipped diagnostic and therapeutic services. Medical leaders know that tomorrow's practice will relate even more closely to the hospital simply because researchers will continue to develop ever more complex costly equipment requiring highly skilled, well-paid technicians to man it and daily making it more difficult for the physician to practice effective medicine without an ever better hospital close at hand.

The trustee who does not accept the responsibility for expansion and remodeling, or who is unable to participate because of the personal contribution he must make in time, talent and funds, should make his chair at the governing board meeting available to another capable leader if the hospital management and medical staff recommend such a program be launched. Otherwise, the trustee would be derelict in his position of public trust.

Hospital management people have the heaviest responsibility. The trustee and physician are essentially "volunteers" insofar as hospital expansion and remodeling are concerned. Being effective in moving the hospital forward to provide the community with better, more comfortable, and safer care while guarding against unnecessary expenditures is the very essence of management. The chief executive officer must take the lead in defining the problem (and the opportunity). To him falls the primary responsibility for setting the effort in motion. He must make every effort to keep the program moving by encouraging maximum participation from key people at the proper time. He should be the first to call for outside assistance to supplement knowhow within the hospital and to initiate cooperative programs with others. He must arrange his work so that he can effectively look far enough ahead to prevent future roadblocks from making hospital expansion and remodeling a crisis instead of a carefully planned, well-scheduled event in the life cycle of a top-quality community center for medical and hospital care.

Chapter II

CLASSIFICATIONS

OWNERSHIP

LIKE their patients, hospitals come in assorted shapes and sizes, and there are many ways to classify them. More than half are voluntary, nonprofit, community hospitals. These institutions, found throughout the nation, are essentially owned and operated as a quasipublic service by the people of the area in which they are situated. Their sole reason for existence is to provide the best of hospital care at the lowest possible cost to the patient.

Benjamin Franklin is credited with the establishment of the first such hospital in the United States. Often religious orders and churches have created hospitals as part of their conviction that the total needs of their congregations included hospital care. Most are guided by a governing board composed of leading successful citizens willing to devote ample time, talent and, frequently, money, to the provision of health facilities for the people of their community. They receive no compensation other than the deep personal satisfaction gained from serving others.

"Nonprofit" needs a word of explanation because it is essentially a legal term widely misinterpreted by other than attorneys. Some hospitals have become major factors in the economy of the community in which they are situated. An annual volume of income and expense in excess of five or six million dollars is not unusual. This level of operation calls for the most careful management, just as is the case with any other business. Budget forecasts, cost accounting, and internal and external audits are a regular occurrence in today's well-managed hospital. Every possible effort is made to stay out of the "red" . . . to stay within predetermined dollar limitations. "Nonprofit" does not mean the hospital need function upon an unsound financial basis. It does mean that no one can pocket the surplus should there be an excess of income over expense. When the hospital shows a "profit," and to be financially sound it should in terms of total income and expense, this money must be used only for the continued improvement of patient care. In California, there is the added stipulation that "profit" beyond 10 per cent of gross expense is illegal and will place the tax-free status of the hospital in jeopardy. This provision seldom proves restrictive because few, if any, nonprofit institutions come anywhere near the ceiling. Three, four, or five per cent is closer to the fact.

"Nonprofit" status confers certain privileges upon the hospital. Most taxes are waived. The corporation may receive gifts which donors are permitted to deduct from their personal or corporate income tax. In return, the nonprofit hospital invariably provides a considerable amount of free and part-pay care to patients unable to pay the full cost of hospitalization. Many services are provided by these organizations which never would be undertaken by an institution operated in the conventional manner of industry for profit.

During the past few years, open-heart surgery has become a frequent occurrence, frequent in the sense that more than 100 medical centers are equipped and staffed to perform this intricate procedure which saves and extends life. The first open-heart surgery case undertaken in any hospital may cost $100,000.00. The hospital never will make a profit economically in this type undertaking, and were it not for the "nonprofit" aspect of the hospital, the advent and utilization of this and most earlier advances in medicine would be restricted to the effort govermental units could make. This would immediately cut back medical progress and force patients with complex illness to queue up at city, county or state hospitals where the services would be completely overtaxed and unable to cope with the load.

Another "nonprofit" plus factor is the ability of capable civic leaders serving on the board of directors of the community institution to shift funds readily within the hospital to meet rapid advances in medicine without making the project a federal proposition. So it is that the nonprofit corporation provides a method for people to pool their resources in solving a community problem beyond the scope of individual ability and yet retain control locally and avoid defaulting to the government.

Government units at the various echelons are the next major operators of hospitals. They may be city, county, state or federal hospitals and usually serve a special segment of the people. For example, a limited number of federal hospitals, operated by the United State Public Health Service, serves the Indian population on various reservations in the West. Military personnel, and sometimes their dependents, are served by Army, Navy and Air Force installations. Most state governments provide facilities for long-term care as in the case of the patient suffering from tuberculosis or from mental illness. When city and county hospitals are available, they usually are established for the care of the patient unable to pay the cost of his care. The Veterans Administration branch of the federal government was designed originally to serve the veteran with a service-connected disability, but over a period of time, in response to political pressure, many thousands of patients are treated in V.A. institutions regardless of the nature or origin of their illness. In contrast to the self-supporting, nonprofit community hospital, governmental hospitals are supported directly by all citizens who pay taxes. Their tax bill includes enough of an assessment to underwrite the cost of all government hospitals.

During recent years, scores of hospitals have been established by private capital as an investment, just as any other business might be set up. Owned and operated to make a profit, most "proprietary" hospitals are relatively small in size and scope of service. Although they represent close to 15 per cent of all hospitals, they provide 3 per cent of all beds. Proprietary hospitals are particularly prevalent in rapidly growing sections of the country where voluntary organizations have been slow in meeting the needs of the expanding population. A not-unusual development finds the small proprietary hospital beset with many difficulties overcome only by conversion to a nonprofit, community status. By its very nature as an organization established to earn a profit for its owner, the proprietary hospital cannot often undertake services that are unduly expensive, or seldom provide care to any except the patient able to pay the full cost of care. In this case, cost also must include income and property taxes plus interest on the capital investment and a profit to the owners. Yet, in many communities there would be no hospital were it not for the entrepreneurs who accumulated the necessary capital and undertook the risk of creating the proprietary hospital.

From among the three major classifications of hospitals, another grouping is made frequently. The great majority of hospitals are general in scope, but a substantial number offer only highly specialized services. There are children's hospitals in many large cities. Occasionally a hospital will devote its entire energy to the treatment of cancer, eye disease and injury, mental illness, T. B., or other limited areas.

The general hospital's objective is to attempt to provide diagnosis and treatment for most illness. Seldom will the hospital's capability fall short of taking care of medical, surgical, obstetrical and pediatric patients suffering from normal illness or injury. As the hospital increases in size, its scope of service usually expands to incorporate round-the-clock emergency treatment, care for the psychiatric patient, rehabilitation units, physical and occupational therapy, social service, pastoral care, education and research and other advanced services.

The specialized hospital, such as mental, chronic or tubercular, is a center for large numbers of patients afflicted with similar disease. Except for children's hospitals, the specialized institutions usually treat the patient with a long-term illness on a free or very limited payment basis, operating costs having been assumed by the taxpayer. Children's hospitals actually are general hospitals for young patients. They are able to do exceptionally fine work for children by gathering together in one organization all the special talent, facilities and supplies best suited to patients age fifteen or less.

SIZE

Hospitals usually are designated by size as well as by ownership and type of service. As you naturally might assume, the greatest number of hospitals are relatively small . . . under fifty beds. A size increases, the number of hospitals in the category decreases.

TEACHING HOSPITALS

Another distinction, of special importance to people contemplating a career in health service, lies in the "teaching" hospital. About 800 hospitals fall into this category, and approximately one-quarter of these are affiliated with university medical schools. Internships and residencies are available only in teaching hospitals approved by the American Medical Association. These institutions also often are the center for training programs offered to potential dietitians, technicians, therapists and medical record librarians. Nurses usually receive a portion of their clinical experience in teaching hospitals, but close to half the schools of nursing are located in hospitals without other major educational responsibilities.

CONVALESCENT HOSPITALS AND NURSING HOMES

The advent of "medicare" has added importance to the role of the convalescent hospital and nursing home. Usually the service available to patients in these institutions is programmed at a somewhat lower level than provided by general hospitals, as the patient is not acutely ill. Care may range from a custodial level to full nursing support for a bed-ridden patient suffering from a chronic disease. However, even when full nursing support is required, the level of technical nursing skill needed is lower than in the acute hospital. Where an acute hospital may have up to half its nursing service personnel in the RN category, the convalescent hospital and nursing home usually require RNs only in a supervisory capacity.

There has been a surge of construction in this field of hospitals in recent years due to "medicare" activities. The majority of institutions are owned and operated by individuals on an investment basis and with the intent to earn a profit. The successful formation and operation of corporations owning many convalescent hospitals suggests that many advantages of chain-operated hotels and motels may find their way into this segment of health care. Unhampered by community pride and motivated by profit consideration, a chain of well-managed convalescent hospitals can carefully select locations with the greatest success potential and, financed in the same manner as other businesses, quickly move in and build the most advantageous-sized unit.

There can be no question that "medicare" will bring about higher operating costs for the owner of the convalescent hospital and nursing home. Federal officials will insist on certain standards being met before they authorize payments for care given medicare patients, and this will affect the entire operation. The possibilities for success in a small independent nursing home or convalescent hospital will become small, they will improve as the size of the unit increases so that the economic advantages of a larger enterprise can be obtained.

To date no one has demonstrated effectively that the law of diminishing returns applies in this field . . . the point of no return in terms of size has not been identified. On the other hand, it is accepted widely in the hospital field that small units face more difficult problems in terms of high cost and low income. Independent investors probably will be less inhibited in exploring mergers which offer opportunities to increase profitability than are not-for-profit organizations where, by definition and tradition, profitability is of secondary concern.

Chapter III

HOW HOSPITALS FUNCTION

GAINING deeper insight into the operation of hospitals will be helpful when it is necessary to expand or remodel. In probing into the organization of hospitals, we will be concerned primarily with "how they work," what the elements are and how various segments function in meeting their responsibilities to patients.

ESSENTIAL ELEMENTS

Every hospital has at least two basic elements and most have four. The medical staff and employee groups are essential. The patient would receive no care without them. Highly desirable for the contribution they make toward better care are governing boards and volunteer workers. It is common practice to have four basic elements within the organization, and it is noteworthy that of these four, employees only are subject to direct supervision in the conventional sense. The essence of a volunteer program is that the participant be permitted to do the work that she herself selects at her time and convenience, accepting of course, that the patient benefits. The director on the governing board also is a volunteer in this regard, and at the same time he represents the controlling factor in the organization. The physician is an independent professional man free to come and go as he sees fit, and subject only to the authority doctors relinquish to colleagues as they are organized into a medical staff.

COMMON GOAL

Obviously this is a complex organization. The hospital is as ready to break apart as a satellite is to fall out of orbit. Very few are the organizations with as high and critical purpose where successful attainment of the objective is so utterly dependent upon people over whom there is little or no direct control. Were it not for the fact that the goal of saving and extending human life is the only reason for the hospital's existence, certainly such a loosely integrated group of individuals, with so wide a diversity of background, would be entirely incapable of functioning smoothly and effectively for an extended time.

CHECKS AND BALANCES

If the best interests of the patient are to be served at all times, the top level of the hospital organization must function with a built-in system of checks and balances not greatly different than those provided in government by the founding fathers of the United States. In practice the medical staff, hospital workers, volunteers and board of directors in the successful hospital do serve as such a system. The chief executive officer provides leadership plus serving as an essential catalytic agent.

In the life cycle of the hospital one element or another will, from time to time, assume a role of greater importance. However, should this continue unchallenged, the system will become unbalanced and will begin to subordinate the interests of the patient to those of the dominating factor. Certainly teamwork is essential. But teamwork alone is not enough, a misguided administrator, doctor, director or employee left unchecked could destroy the ability of the hospital to serve effectively the health needs of the community.

With little difficulty, the chief executive following Parkinson's law could overdevelop management in terms of people, expense and control. A few particularly ambitious, well-organized specialists could close the doors to generalists, or vice versa. A dollar-only-oriented director could block the installation of the newest life-saving equipment solely on the grounds that it will be an economic burden. Union-motivated stewards easily can serve the union at the expense of the patient by stirring up grievances and striking for big benefits. All of these situations have occurred, and will occur again at the expense of patient care unless the informal system of checks and balances is at work. Out of balance, the effectiveness of the organization is destroyed, as far as employees and employer and the patient are concerned. It is also destroyed as a doctor's workshop and a needed civic asset required to attract and retain business and industry.

Yet, it is in this organizational sense that hospitals are markedly different from most other institutions with which we are familiar, other than our national government. We've had it drilled into us that an effective organization has but one head. Those of us who work with, or for, a hospital have to unlearn this bit of theory. The hospital is a "three-headed" organization, and never does one head always speak with authority for the others, nor does one consistently issue directives to be obeyed without question by the others. However, by the same token, there are times when it is fitting, proper and indeed essential for either the medical staff, board or management to speak with authority and to assume comparable responsibility for the hospital.

Obviously, the only way a three-headed organization can be anything but a monster is when all three have identical objectives, understand and have confidence in one another. When this occurs, the old saw of "two heads are better than one" is upgraded as three heads working well together are able to overcome almost any obstacle in their common determination to provide the patient with the best possible care. The hospital organization then becomes a thing of beauty, wonderful to observe in action.

This achievement is no small task.

Doctors, to be effective, must function as individuals in relation to their patients.

The doctor is evaluating information constantly, arriving at his own decision, carrying out a course of action and assuming responsibility for the outcome. This is what he does every day, all day (and sometimes half the night). But, in the hospital, he is placed in a situation where, to achieve the objectives of the organization, he has to curb his individualistic tendencies and function as a member of a group. In the patient's room he must be an individual. In the hospital corridor a minute later he might be called upon to function as a member of the hospital medical staff, possibly accepting group decisions, and occasionally even initiating disciplinary action where his colleagues might be concerned.

This is not an easy transition to recognize and achieve.

Frequently, hospital trustees are successful businessmen and the recognized leaders of industrial or commercial companies. When they assume their other roles as members of the hospital board of directors, they are confronted with this three-headed organization which operates in a manner foreign to that with which they are familiar. It is sometimes difficult to make this adjustment during a luncheon meeting of the board, when the morning and afternoon call for an entirely different role. Particularly, is it difficult for the doctor and the civic leader when no one takes the time to explain this "abnormal" situation. Hospital executives need not only to understand this important aspect of the hospital, but also they must work unceasingly to achieve maximum acceptance of the concept by all members of the organization.

How does this concept work in practice? The medical staff and administration may recognize the need to expand hospital facilities well before the board of directors is conscious of the problem. The administrator, working with key physicians, is able to alert the board to the need. When this group is ready to move in on the problem, it may determine the scope of expansion in terms of plant, equipment and dollars, and in turn obtain medical staff financial support as the foundation for a successful community-wide hospital fund drive.

Leadership may be shifted several times. It is unlikely that either management, board or staff will retain a dominant position in the organization. Throughout the definition and solution of this problem, the effective executive officer must be able to guide the leaders through these changes as all elements of the organization keep their basic objective in mind . . . better care for the patient.

Assuming that the top level of the organization does function as presented, we will turn briefly to other questions. Although it is not difficult to achieve widespread agreement on the basic objective of the hospital . . . providing patient care . . . various elements of the organization may differ widely in their understanding of the scope of patient care as it is related to the hospital. Disagreement as to the method of attaining the goal(s) and timing might be expected as normal corollaries. Communication alone offers a major stumbling block when too many people are involved in so complex a problem.

Participation in definition of the hospital's scope of operation, in methods and timing by the medical staff, board and management, may not be the only method of obtaining agreement, but it is certainly effective. In practice, a joint conference committee is the usual vehicle for attainment of effective participation. However, management must make a continuous determined effort to obtain active interest and support of immediate and long-term objectives through informal channels and personal contact with doctors and directors. When leaders of the board and staff join in this effort at the country club as well as around the conference table, the patient's welfare may well become and remain the primary evaluating factor in the conduct of hospital affairs.

It needs to be stated, clearly and definitely, that in the lower echelons of the organization, more conventional patterns are followed. If carried beyond the policy-making level of the board of directors and the executive committee of the staff, the system of checks and balances could lead to complete frustration among hospital employees. Once basic policy has been determined and management has delegated the authority and responsibility essential to achieve the desired objective(s), then by requiring carefully prepared plans including positive action, recommendations, and following progress through regular and special reports, the board will be most assured of attaining its objectives.

Departing from the policy level often is an easier path for the board and executive committee to follow than to adhere strictly to delegation of operating responsibility and authority. Yet, the record is clear. Temptation to dip into management should be resisted by the policy-forming groups, and the chief executive must not follow the course of least resistance by passing the buck on management affairs to the board.

In turn, regardless of the size of the hospital, if the management is to obtain maximum effective utilization of all personnel resources, the executive officer must be able to delegate authority and responsibility to his key people. And, equally important, he must provide meaningful follow-up supervision.

Although some Catholic hospitals now have advisory boards, and the trend is toward their establishment, many effectively combine the function of governing board and management in the persons of the sisters who own and operate the institutions.

In large measure, government hospitals function as division or department of an echelon of government without a governing board. Some, however, do have a small advisory or supervisory group elected by the citizens or appointed by elected officials.

Proprietary hospitals granted a corporate charter, of course, are required to have a legally constituted board of directors. Usually this is made up of the major stockholders and is not intended to represent the community or interests other than those of the investors.

Chapter IV

THE PLANNING
AND EXPANSION TEAM

INITIATION OF EXPANSION

IN many hospitals, it is the physician who is first to call for action in expansion and remodeling. He cannot get his patient admitted or, when he does, diagnostic and therapeutic facilities may be lacking.

Often the chief executive officer presses for solutions to problems which must be solved if patients are to receive safe and comfortable care at reasonable cost.

Inspecting officials from governmental or voluntary agencies have persuaded hospitals to institute construction in order to correct substandard conditions. Unfortunately, due to lack of financial resources, expansion and remodeling frequently is delayed until a crisis is at hand.

BUILDING COMMITTEE

When embarking on a construction program, it is quite important to form a strong building committee. The normal project will extend over a period of at least one or two years and then may be followed by another and another. From the governing board should come the chairman. It will be very helpful if he has had prior experience in major construction programs. The medical staff should be represented and physician members selected with care. They need not be the elected representative of their colleagues, but they should be respected and they should be willing to devote sufficient time to the program.

If the committee is fortunate, it will include people with experience in banking, law and insurance. Management of the hospital should be represented by the chief executive officer and the top-level employees he deems necessary. Other people with special knowledge may be called in on an advisory basis to bring to bear the best possible *technical* contribution when planning reaches the detail stage involved in departmental design and equipment selection within their field of competency.

A general duty nurse, for example, may make an excellent contribution to the design of a medication room; she obviously would be at a considerable disadvantage in coping with problems of site selection or the layout of the dietary department.

The committee will require the assistance of an able secretary as all decisions should be recorded. Numerous meetings will be held. Notices and other written material will seem endless. As one planner noted, "When the weight of the paper is equal to the estimated weight of the structure, ground will be broken!"

PROFESSIONAL ADVISERS

One of the early and often difficult tasks will be to select and retain competent professional advisors. Few architects specialize in the narrow field of hospital design. When they do, they evidence a tendency to develop a particular style and to adapt it to almost every hospital they work on. Perhaps this is just as well. By personally inspecting hospitals designed by the individual or firm, the committee can come away with an excellent idea of how their particular project will shape up. And there is a reasonable possibility that the structure might work out very well inasmuch as past errors may be known and avoided.

On the other hand, a competent local architect who has successfully handled other projects of at least equal scope might provide the best answer. A responsible member of the committee should be delegated the task of checking personally the candidate's earlier projects, and he should check personally with the owners. Although the reference check may be handled by telephone or letter, an on-the-spot verification is most revealing.

In a building project as highly specialized as a hospital and involving a substantial sum of money, it is an excellent idea to include an experienced hospital consultant on the planning team from its inception. A competent consultant will earn his fee (usually less than 2 per cent of the cost of the project) many times, both in the matter of planning economically and later, as this results in effective and efficient functioning of the plant and equipment. Futher, it is most reassuring to those providing capital funds for construction to know that an outside, impartial, objective expert is helping with the plan. There are times when an "outsider" is needed to stop grandiose empire builders.

Patients are reassured when their first impression of the hospital is favorable.

Not to be overlooked on the planning team are other important specialists. Engineers who work with the architect play a vital role. Obviously a hospital is much different from a department store, school building or factory. Most buildings primarily are shells within which is placed the equipment used to produce goods or services. Usually the cost of equipment outweighs the cost of the structure.

This position is reversed for the hospital. It is most important that the structure be engineered very carefully. Errors made in design and carried into construction are very difficult to correct in hospitals. In a factory, a new machine can be installed with relative ease. It is exceedingly difficult to replace concealed inadequate or improper electrical lines, plumbing, heating and ventilating equipment after solid, fire-resistant walls, floors and ceilings are in place in the hospital.

Unless engineers are competent and exercise care, they can be misled by the average requirements of the hospital. For instance, some have specified inadedquate plumbing lines into the laundry. They may check the requirements of the washing equipment and find that it is necessary to supply an average of "X" gallons of hot water in order to launder "X" pounds of linen per patient per day. But in operation, in order to be efficient and economical, the several washers each may call for hundreds of gallons of hot water in a *peak* demand of a few minutes while the machines are going through numerous wash and rinse cycles. It may develop that the peak load in the laundry coincides with a similar peak demand for hot water in the dish-washing room and also in central sterile supply. If all related peak-load requirements are not thought through with care, the basic water-heating need can be underestimated and incoming supply lines and outgoing drainage facilities also might be inadequate.

Chapter V

TOTAL DESIGN FACTORS

BETTER FACILITIES

PERHAPS a "standard" hospital will evolve some day. At this time there is very little conformity in hospital design and considerable controversy. In recent years, one school of architects has become the proponent of circular-designed hospitals. Another would see all hospitals utilize the "double-corridor" plan. Still others recommend single-corridor, Maltese-cross, square, rectangular, "H"-shape and so on. With regard to the type of accommodation for patients, there are staunch advocates for having all rooms single, some recommend double. A mixture of the single, double and four-bed is common.

Lacking a widespread consensus of "expert" opinion as a firm guide, the committee will have to resolve these questions for itself. A conservative decision would be to avoid extremes in design that happen to be fashionable at the time of planning. There might be excellent use made of both the single and double-corridor design, using the former in areas of high activity and the latter in areas of normal activity rather than to jump completely in either direction.

Every design is a compromise. If planners want to conserve nurse time and strive for utmost convenience to the nurse, double-corridor plans will accomplish this. If maximum quiet is desired for the patient to expedite his recovery, the single-corridor approach is preferred. Some planners use the double-corridor design for such units as intensive care, operating suite, labor and delivery suite, x-ray and laboratory where there is a great deal of activity and quiet for the patient is not an issue. Double-corridor refers to a design with patients located on the perimeter while service units are placed in an interior space with corridors separating the service area from the patient rooms. On normal patient-care nursing units, they may then use the single corridor to insure maximum quiet by removing busy service centers from the immediate bedside area.

A related question is the size of the basic nursing unit in terms of the number of patients. The number of patients per nursing unit has steadily increased in recent years. There are several reasons why this has occurred. In general, the larger the nursing unit, the more effective is the utilization of the skilled registered nurse. Registered nurses have been in short supply for many years. The outlook for the shortage being alleviated is dismal, and it may become even more acute. While the number of RNs has decreased in relation to the population, a number of mechanical features have become available, which if utilized fully, conserve the time of the nurse. These include the following:

1. The all-electric bed. Most patients are able to adjust the spring and mattress for comfort as often as they like without calling for nursing assistance. Being able to lower the bed from its normal high nursing level down close to the floor makes it possible for many patients to get in and out of bed without assistance, giving them a desired feeling of independence early in their recovery, and often speeding their discharge.

2. The electronic intercom significantly reduces nurse walking time as many patients' calls are for information rather than for personal service. When calls are for service, the nurse arrives at the bedside better prepared to help the patient and may avoid return walking to obtain a supply item needed by the patient but unknown to the nurse were it not for the intercom.

3. The telephone, now frequently found at almost every bedside, is a great convenience to the patient and saves considerable nursing time formerly expended in relaying messages.

4. Placing bathroom accommodations adjacent to every patient room also is a great patient convenience and nurse time-saver, particularly when all-electric beds are used. Patients dislike using the bed pan. They prefer to be indeddpendent of the nurse in this regard as soon as possible. The all-electric bed with its high-low feature, speeds this welcomed transition.

5. Concentrating the patients needing most care in specially designed intensive-care units reduces the burden on nursing personnel in normal patient care sections of the hospital.

UTILIZATION HIGHER —
LOWER OPERATING COSTS

The total effect of these factors is to make it possible to increase safely the distance from nursing station to the bedside of the most remote patient. Years ago the rule of thumb was that this key distance factor should not exceed forty feet. Not more than twenty-five patients could be located within forty feet of a nursing station. Today distance can reach 140 feet if maximum use is made of the five factors listed above and 100 patients can be gathered around a single nursing unit.

The primary reason planners increase the size of the nursing unit is to achieve concentration of RN personnel as opposed to dispersing these scarce, skilled people over a large number of small units. Greater concentration of RNs permits more flexibility in their assignments so that patients needing RN attention are more likely to receive it than if available RNs are distributed over a larger number of units. Flexibility may become a critical factor during evenings and nights and on weekends and holidays when the number of RNs is at its lowest point . . . These periods add up to more than 70 per cent of the total time patients require care.

Concentrating patients and personnel in larger units has other important benefits. Supervision of a large unit calls for higher quality of supervision, justifies a higher compensation standard and attracts able leaders. It is possible to select and train able nurses in management or to reverse the procedure and select and train lay personnel in nursing, the net effect in either case being to upgrade the quality of supervision and management of nursing personnel. With patient care dependent upon a heterogeneous group consisting of persons with a wide variety of skills, education and experience ranging from a virtually untrained nurse's aide to the top-flight RN with a college degree, quality of management available on the nursing unit becomes a vital factor in determining the caliber of care patients receive. Likewise, management effectiveness on the nursing unit has considerable bearing upon the cost of care. A corollary factor is that people of lesser skills, such as the clerk, can be more effective in a larger unit than in a smaller one, particularly at other than during the daytime shifts. A clerk can be more efficient on a nursing unit of 100 patients at 2:00 A. M. than can four clerks on four units of twenty-five beds each. There is not enough for her to do on the smaller unit. Yet there are functions she can handle well and relieve the RN of nonprofessional duties so that skilled nurses can be at the bedside instead of at the desk.

Each nursing unit requires a number of supporting services in close proximity; medication room, clean and soiled utility, pantry, linen, elevators, lounge, restroom and often a classroom and treatment rooms. These can be grouped effectively using less space and lower cost as the size of the nursing unit increases. Mechanical aids such as the pneumaitc tube system and the dumbwaiter can be used to greater capacity as the number of patients served per unit increases.

In all these facilities, including the patient room, planners can avoid the criticism of future users of the hospital by not being overly economical in allocating space. If dimensions of the patient room are tight, the problem of recent years may be repeated. Patients are growing taller. Hospital beds are longer than they used to be. A foot in length added to the bed in a small room results in overcrowding. Nurses may have to move the furniture each time a stretcher has to be brought into the room. This is wasteful and costly. When repeated for the life of the building, added operating expense will far more than offset initial cost of more square footage of floor space.

It is unnecessary to state that the patient room, nursing unit and all departments of the hospital should be designed and equipped with every proven time-saving device available even though this makes the problem of financing more difficut. It is a well known fact that wages and salaries may equal or exceed 70 per cent of the initial construction and equipment cost. Dollars invested in well-designed, better-equipped and adequately-sized facilities return excellent dividends each year in better care at lower cost.

The space factor carries over into corridor, elevators and other areas. Eight foot corridors are common. However, new longer beds cannot be moved from a room and turned into the corridor without extra handling unless the width is at least nine feet. Scarred walls and damaged beds also result from tightly designed rooms and corridors. Undersized elevators pose similar problems. The added cost differential to build and maintain an extra square foot of floor space is relatively nominal. An extra square foot of concrete, floor covering and ceiling may represent the greatest bargain of the entire project if considered in relation to operating costs, projected for the normal life of the building.

Well designed easily operated electric beds increase patient comfort and safety and reduce the demand for skilled employees.

FUTURE EXPANSION

A maximum effort should be made to plan and build with definite provision for future expansion. The least than can be done is to have footings, foundation and supporting structure engineered to carry more floors if expansion ever should be necessary. If at all possible, provision should be included for added vertical transportation. Key diagnostic therapeutic and service departments should be oversized to permit equipment to be added as needed. If another expansion phase is imminent and capital limited, it may be feasible and desirable to "shell in" extra bare space which later may be finished quickly when required.

Many hospitals have been forced to acquire property at steep prices as expansion called for more land. Farsighted hospital executives initiate purchase of key property when the opportunity is present. In some instances, this has been in outlying areas and has become the site of much needed satellite hospitals.

Chapter VI

INTERIOR DESIGN

"THIS room has warmth. It seems friendly, inviting."

"I like the colors here. They show good taste."

These and similar reactions have been heard by hospital people with increasing frequency in recent years. Americans have developed, to an unprecedented degree, a sensitivity to arrangement, appearance, and atmosphere.

This appeal to the eye and the mind is something hospital people should not overlook. The public certainly has not ignored it. In increasing numbers, people purchase well-designed automobiles, shop at ultra-modern supermarkets, and patronize hotels which have been constructed or remodeled to meet the newest standards of eye appeal. Even banks and office buildings have discovered that it pays to have excellent interior design work done. I believe it can prove a good investment, too, in a hospital.

Few people want to go to a hospital. This feeling of reluctance can be accentuated if the hospital plant is cold, drab and depressing.

We are striving constantly to reassure patients, to give them a feeling of well-being, and to replace their sense of despair with optimism and hope. I have been surprised to note how helpful the proper use of color, the wise choice of fabrics and skillful arrangements of furnishings can be in creating a feeling of reassurance in patients from the moment they enter a hospital. This "plus" for patients, however, is not the only value derived from creating a warm and comfortable atmosphere in a hospital. It can pay in dollars and cents, too.

[33]

OBTAINING PROFESSIONAL ADVICE

It has been my experience in hospital projects involving an expenditure of some many millions of dollars that the investment made in professional services in this area is returned many times in savings on initial purchase plus the long-term economy of lower maintenance cost of properly selected interiors.

We must be certain at the outset that we do not stumble into a major pitfall. Specifically, we must not make the mistake of thinking that "functionalism," which is given us by the architect, is the same as "interior designing," which is a highly important supplementary service.

A hospital can be exceptionally well-planned from the functional point of view, and yet almost ugly and depressing to all who use or benefit from its highly efficient work areas. Now, this is not an argument against good functional planning, when we never are really satisfied with even the best. It is, however, intended to focus attention on the fact that excellent interior design is not only compatible with the smoothest work flow pattern, but should be considered as a necessity that effectively, efficiently, and economically supports the functional plan.

There may be a serious, widening gap between the completed work of the hospital architect and the actual operation of many areas of the hospital. While this gap is not so apparent in the operating room, x-ray department or laundry, it may be quite obvious in the public areas, and of real concern in the nursing units. I refer to the pressing need to ease the mind of the patient as well as to meet his physical problems; to reassure him from the moment he steps in the front door; and to have him see for himself that the hospital cares about him and his interest.

The architect strives to achieve this goal in the very design of the building. Administrative people attempt to accomplish the same objective in their selection of furniture, draperies and related items. As in other fields, however, there has been a tremendous increase in the almost daily changes of the thousands of articles and materials which can be considered for hospital use.

Highly specialized knowledge is required to cope with problems of interior space, planning, lighting, mill work and cabinet details. In addition, color, fabrics, furniture, floor and wall coverings are essential considerations that require the participation of experts. We are becoming increasingly aware of fine paintings and sculpture as humanizing influences on our interiors. All interior items should not be obtained haphazardly but should be integrated carefully into a harmonious, effective, economic unity.

It seems to me that, in general, hospitals do a reasonable acceptable job of carrying out this concept in most areas—surgery, for example. Hospital planners know this area well. They are knowledgeable regarding floor space requirements, lighting, air conditioning, operating room equipment and the like. This knowledge, however, is not always brought to bear in public areas where the patients and their visitors may be more inclined to judge the atmosphere of a hospital.

The handling of such areas as cafeterias, snack bars, lounges, offices, and waiting rooms affects the attitude of people toward the hospital. The able administrator is aware of this fact and realizes that only the more gifted individual can deal effectively with the intricacies of such problems as specialized lighting and color coordination. How, then, does one meet this problem effectively and economically?

At least two courses of action are available. It is important to make an analysis of all the factors related to the particular hospital under consideration before reaching a decision on which course is best. Varying degrees of assistance may be obtained from manufacturers and distributors. Producers of paint, office equipment, furnishings, and furniture frequently have decorators on their staff for the primary purpose of making their services available to customers.

Merchandising firms often take considerable pride in the caliber of advice they are able to offer hospitals. Such organizations may be local, regional or national in scope. Usually no direct charge is made for the services of these people. It is, of course, apparent that the dispenser of the service must obtain some sales income to carry the expense inherent in offering the decorators' time and talent. This income may be gained by way of commissions or mark-up on the cost of goods sold.

Personal inspection of the work done for other customers, and a close check of references is advisable. Some assurance should be obtained regarding the stability of the organization so that the work will not be delayed unduly by illness, change in personnel or other factors.

A second approach is to obtain the services of a competent professional interior designer or design firm. Architects often provide this service for an additional fee. Where they do not offer the service, architects may encourage their clients to retain competent professional advice. This may pose a real problem, however, as today almost anyone may decide overnight that he or she is a fully qualified interior designer.

GUIDE TO SELECTION

As a guide to selection, I would suggest that consideration be given to developing what might, for lack of a better term, be called "specification." Here is an outline of factors which might be of help in assessing various professional designs:

1. Is the firm well-established and unquestionably successful? Does it have a record of repeat business?

2. Does it have experience in a variety of interior design situations covering many of these categories:

Cafeteria	Chapel
Snack Bar	Laundry
Office Building	Library
Hotel	Education Facility
Gift Shop	Scientific Laboratory
Drugstore	

3. Is continuity of service assured? The firm should be able to give complete assurance that, once underway, the project will be completed on schedule with no interruption tolerated (because of illness, other business, vacations, death, etc.). Availability for future consultation is desirable.

4. Does the firm use a professional and ethical approach with entire compensation based solely on a fee for services? (No commission, mark-up, cut, "kick-back," etc.).

5. Does the organization include architects and draftsmen,

competent decorators, designers and specification writers?

The finished "product" of the consultant would, in most cases, include scale drawings of plans, elevations as well as details, special lighting, mill and cabinet work. Either the drawings or specifications, or both, should include paint or wall-covering selections, drapery fabrics, upholstery materials and floor coverings. Most importantly, these drawings and specifications must be of an exactness, quality and caliber that will permit accurate cost estimates, as well as equitable competitive bidding. This is essential to the total economy of the project.

Providing ample room may prove to be a very good investment of hospital funds.

6. Is the firm qualified to analyze work flow and methods, so that office furniture and equipment selection, as well as layout and space utilization, will provide optimum working conditions?

I would suggest also the development of guides towards a fuller understanding of the scope of the work and the responsibilities of the hospital, as well as of those of the interior design form or other consultants.

Interior design people say, and I would agree, that whenever the services of an interior designer are retained at an early age of a project, their effectiveness has been greater. The earlier the development of a team concept among the architects, engineers, interior designer and the hospital, the more fruitful the relationship. The interior designer may be brought in a later stage, however, well after the architects and engineers have performed a major portion of their work, and most of their plans are already prepared. Even at such a point, an interior designer's effectiveness well may constitute a major contribution.

At whatever point the interior designers are introduced into the project, their fundamental function should be the integration of all interior components, to aid in attaining the hospital's basic objectives. The interior designer's role is to achieve unity and serenity of all the interior components, while maintaining or improving the functional and efficient elements that are essential to the hospital.

ASSIGNMENT CHECKLIST

The following points constitute the beginning of an informal checklist of the items one should require of an interior designer:

1. Submit color schedules for all interior painting and decoration, floor covering, tile, marble and terrazzo.

2. Submit layouts of furniture. Indicate positions on floor plans.

3. Select and specify for competitive bidding furniture, carpeting and furnishings. Prepare furniture and furnishings schedules and catalogues.

4. Consult with the hospital and architect on modifications or changes on interiors, as possible improvements may suggest themselves during the progress of work.

5. Assist in supervising, expediting and purchasing as may be required.

6. Submit analyses and recommendations of all bids.

7. Prepare and submit budget estimates prior to the call for bids.

8. Begin and complete consulting work on pre-arranged dates.

9. Receive payment as work progresses, in a specified number of equal monthly installments.

10. Expenses, other than fees, require prior approval of administrator.

11. A specific member of the decorating firm assigned to head the project. All work must be reviewed personally by the principal.

12. The total sum expended for furniture and furnishings may not exceed a sum as agreed upon in advance.

Many professional interior design firms prefer to work on an hourly-fee basis. They may consider it unethical to be compensated by commission. Many firms consider any arrangement of this type as interfering with the objective standard they desire to maintain in the client's interest.

INTERIOR AND EXTERIOR EXCELLENCE

Highly favorable public reaction is the result and reward of this effort to demonstrate actively and visually an interest in the patient. A vast store of information and experience is available to hospitals, to make the hospital appealing, interesting and quietly reassuring to the patient through its clean, orderly, attractive appearance. It is possible that hospitals may be considered remiss in their responsibilities unless a determined effort is made to close the gap existing between the basic architectural design of the structure and the purchase of furnishings, furniture and equipment.

Just as the interior designer's work will augment the architect's concepts within the building, so will the work of a qualified landscape architect make a valuable contribution in helping attain a pleasing, restful setting for the building.

Leaders of industry and commerce have demonstrated the hardheaded business value of achieving complete unity in function, landscaping and interior design as an aid in attracting and retaining better employees, as well as creating the most effective visual appeal for their clients.

In the hospital field we have these most desirable goals, plus the even more basic objective of reassuring our patients and helping them achieve a feeling of well-being from the first moment they turn to the hospital for care.

Chapter VII

MONEY-SAVING TIPS

AS most hospitals do not regularly undertake major expansion and remodeling projects, experience gained during construction is not always passed along to succeeding executives, doctors and trustees. Here are some important money-saving tips, to remember that may not have been passed along from a previous expansion.

1. Use time to the hospital's advantage in calling for bids. In many areas, contractors are likely to bid a major job when timing is such that they can keep their crews working during inclement weather. If inquiry discloses this is a significant factor, planning may be scheduled so that bidding and construction will permit the contractor to get the building under roof or out of the ground before bad weather.

2. Allow sufficient time for careful bidding. When contractors are in doubt due to haste, they may pad the estimate to afford themselves ample protection against possible error.

3. The last hours of bidding usually are very hectic for the contractor. Subcontractors may submit revised quotations up to the last possible minute, adding to the possibility of error. If errors occur, more often than not the hospital will suffer. Some hospitals have helped the general contractor, and themselves, by setting an unusual bid-closing time such as postmarked 12:00 (midnight). Most of the subcontractor activity falls off after the close of the normal working day. Major suppliers close their offices. The general contractor then has enough time to put his final figure together with full accuracy and complete assurance. The hospital benefits.

4. When permitted, it is sound policy to incorporate a reasonable penalty clause for delayed completion of construction. (If Hill-Harris funds are involved, this is not possible.) A reasonable penalty is the cost of interest on the funds tied up by the

project, reduced to a per-diem basis. If the total cost of construction is one million, interest at 6 per cent per year would equal $60 thousand, or $164 per day. Every day beyond the scheduled completion date of the construction actually costs the hospital that amount of money as the structure is not available for use. The penalty will stimulate the contractor to give the hospital job the careful attention it must have if it is to be completed on schedule without penalty to him.

5. Bring outside resource people in early rather than late. This will offer the maximum opportunity for them to make their contribution in know-how and will minimize the possibility time-consuming changes must be made at a critical period. The possibility of error will be reduced.

6. Everyone recognizes that providing sufficient space for parking cars is a must. It is not apparent that the *rate of growth* in the use of the automobile always has been projected far enough into the future to insure that the hospital will *continue* to have sufficient parking space. Easy access from parking lots is quite important, otherwise drivers invariably will tie up space at entrances to the hospital while tending to real or imagined emergencies. Traffic flow in the parking area is worth careful study. Planners have been eliminating low concrete or wood barriers between isles of cars as they have been recognized to constitute hazards to persons walking to and from their cars. Bright illumination of the parking area may be quite important in some urban areas. The incidence of mugging and theft in parking lots is increasing. Ample light has become a safety measure.

7. It is very important that an experienced, able, detail-oriented person cross-check plans and specifications in the final stage of planning to pick up errors and omissions. An undersized doorway can create a serious bottleneck. It costs no more to specify the correct size. A door unwittingly may be planned to swing in such a way that it blocks access to a related activity. Until the entire plan has evolved, this may not be apparent. Draftsmen sometimes become too accustomed to using right (or left) hand door swing as this is the basic design and overlook exceptions at certain points in the building which require a change. Unless each single detail is checked, the number of errors will be most surprising and costly to correct as change orders during construc-

tion. This is equally true for windows, lights, switches, plumbing, ventilating, air conditioning; every mechanical feature.

8. Construction change orders usually are very costly. Sometimes a contractor can tell from a poorly designed and loosely specified building plan that many change orders will be required once construction is under way. He may get the job by a low bid, planning to make his profit, and a handsome one, through change orders when he no longer has to bid competitively against other contractors.

9. Every major building project must have adequate, careful on-site supervision from an experienced, honest, independent man in the employ of the hospital to be certain that plans and specifications are followed with no deviation unless approved in writing by the owner. Substandard materials and poor workmanship can be covered over rapidly if this is the intent, and, unfortunately, it is all too often.

10. Allow ample latitude in the specifications for color selection of paint, title, floor covering and the like in order to avoid either unduly restricting interior design or calling for costly change orders during construction.

11. As the project nears completion, it may be possible to work out a pre-acceptance schedule with the contractor so the hospital can begin to occupy certain vital areas of the building in advance of others. If the contractor knows the need, he may be able to assign crews accordingly at no added cost to anyone.

12. Carefully explore several different methods of financing. Various possibilities are detailed in Chapter XIII. Hospitals represent a more desirable loan candidate today than ever before. (There was a time when insurance companies, banks and underwriters did not want to have a hospital loan in the portfolios.) A fraction of a per cent of interest over a long term on a large loan can equal a very sizeable amount of money.

13. Much can be gained by erecting a full-size model patient room for careful evaluation by everyone concerned before the final design is frozen. The great majority of people have not had sufficient experience with blueprints to visualize the completed room. Errors in the model room phase can be detected easily and corrected quickly. Hospital people welcome the opportunity to inspect the model room and to express their opinions. Later,

after the building is in use, there is more of a feeling of having been involved in the planning and far less tendency to criticize.

14. It should be recognized at the outset that, regardless of the care with which the building has been designed and constructed, it will draw criticism. To some it is very self-satisfying to be able to point to the location of a particular light switch and find fault with it. Usually, if critics knew all the reasons, they would have reached the same conclusion as the planners. The greater the degree of involvement by opinion leaders in the planning stage, the less unnecessary and destructive criticism on completion.

15. Hospital people touring during construction can be a helpful way to nurture a feeling of involvement. This appeals to a basic desire of many people to be well informed *in advance* of others. It also may stimulate their interest and may help to spread a desirable positive note through the community during construction.

16. During construction and upon completion of the project, an updated set of all plans and specifications should be obtained for later use by the maintenance department. Changes are inevitable during construction. Unless they are accurately detailed and preserved, hospital people will have many anxious hours attempting to locate a pipeline or other mechanical feature that is nowhere near the position originally called for in the blueprints.

17. Polaroid photos of pipe and conduit can be taken before they are hidden by walls, then dated and catalogued to great future advantage.

18. Major savings and better equipment are highly likely if certain specialized equipment is *NOT* included in the general contract and is made the subject of separate specification, separate bid and separate installation. Communication equipment provides an excellent example of why this is true.

Not many years ago, the patient called the nurse by pulling a cord that activated a light over his corridor door. This equipment was simple and included in the general contract. Today's nurse-patient electronic intercom control system may also include remote control entertainment—TV, piped music and closed circuit TV capability for patient education. Outside the patient room extensive communication equipment may encompass individual pocket transistorized radio receivers, surveillance TV for security control, extensions of the closed circuit educational TV system plus complete piped music and public address systems.

The design and installation of an efficient complete hospital communication package may strain the capability of architects, electrical engineers and contractors and may well be better handled outside the general contract. This should result in better design . . . better function . . . and may produce important savings as there is no need to pay a general contractor for the installation when it can be handled directly by the manufacturer.

Other comparable situations are found in sterilizer, food service, elevator and x-ray equipment where carefully spelled out specifications pit manufacturers against one another in the design and bid process to the advantage of the hospital instead of having the benefits of a soundly conceived competitive situation accrue only to the general contractor after he has been awarded the contract.

19. It is very helpful to have a comprehensive checklist established as soon as construction is underway to provide an organized method of keeping essential assignments in focus. An example follows.

TARGET DATE	PROJECT	ASSIGNED TO	DATE COMPLETED
June 1	Beds out to bid _____		
June 15	Nurse-call system out to bid _____		
June 25	Departmental space needs presented _____		
July 1	Bids on beds received _____		
July 1	Food and linen service distribution system finalized _____		
July 1	Complete list of gift opportunities _____		
July 15	Nurse-call system bids received _____		
July 15	Interior design (color selection) _____		
July 15	Exterior color selection _____		
July 15	Food service equipment out to bid _____		
July 27	Space allocation finalized and preliminary drawings begun _____		
August 2	Bed contract awarded _____		
August 2	Nurse-call system contract awarded _____		
August 2	Carpeting and furniture bids sent out _____		

Target Date	Project	Assigned To	Date Completed
August 27	Additional linen supply determined _____		
August 27	Housekeeping equipment out to bid _____		
August 27	Food service equipment orders placed _____		
August 31	Preliminary remodeling drawings presented ___		
September 1	Carpeting contract awarded _____		
September 1	Mercury article—gift opportunities _____		
September 15	Furniture orders placed _____		
September 28	Housekeeping equipment orders placed _____		
September 28	Final remodeling drawings approved _____		
October 1	Final employee staffing budget _____ decisions completed _____		
October 1	Review rate structure and send out official notices _____		
October 1	Complete patient care polices and procedures for Memorial West _____		
October	Tour site (house staff, Employee Advisory Committee) _____		
October	City Council tour of inspection _____		
October	Memorial Hospital Foundation Board tour of inspection _____		
October	Board of Directors tour of inspection _____		
October	Board of Trustees Semi-annual Meeting and tour of inspection _____		
October	Executive Medical Committee tour of inspection		
October 1	Operating budget complete_____		
October 1	Equipment purchase completed _____		
October 15	Check to see if ordered: envelopes, letterheads, etc. _____		
October 15	Television receiver bids sent out _____		
October 15	Remodeling drawings and specifications out to bid _____		
November 1	All plaques ordered _____		
November 1	All positions assigned _____		
November 1	Hospital organization chart revised _____		
November 1	Letterheads printed and on the shelf _____		
November 1	Patient book development underway _____		
November 1	Television receiver contract awarded _____		
November 15	Moving plans finalized _____		
November 15	Forms printed _____		
November 15	Telephone book printed _____		
November 15	Complete plans for open house _____		
November 15	Prepare open house signs _____		
November 15	Volunteer guide training program paper work completed and guides selected _____		

TARGET DATE	PROJECT	ASSIGNED TO	DATE COMPLETED
November 15	Dedication plans complete and speaker obtained _____		
November 15	Volunteer guides begin training _____		
November 15	Contract for January 3 clean-up _____		
November 15	Open house signs to printer _____		
November 29	1966 vacations reviewed (discourage January and February for selected employees, supervisors and department heads _____		
November 29	Employee orientation and training _____		
December 6	Contract or arrange for guard duty _____		
December 6	Special house organ issue _____		
December 6	Parking areas assigned (visitors, employees, doctors) _____		
December 6	Guide schedule complete, printed and distributed _____		
December 6	Remodeling contracts awarded _____		
December 13	Dedication plans, complete assignments accepted _____		
December 13	Dedication invitations _____		
December 13 1966	Notify medical staff and employees of opening _		
January 3-14	Equipment and supplies uncrated and placed in position _____		
January 3-14	Major clean-up _____		
January 3	Twenty-four guard duty established to function until occupancy _____		
January 3	Supplement (newspaper issue) _____		
January 3	Open house agenda printed and distributed ___		
January 3	Dry run plan completed _____		
January 7	Open house signs in place _____		
January 7	Volunteer guides complete training _____		
January 7	Rehab moving plans printed and distributed __		
January 7	All plaques installed _____		
January 7	Invitations mailed _____		
January 10	Check out equipment with contractor's representatives _____		
January 14	Dry run _____		
January 14	All supplies and equipment in place _____		
January 14	Preview—V. I. P. reception and tour _____		
January 17	Public open house _____		
January 17	Dedication _____		
January 24	Clean-up _____		
January 31	Transfer eligible patients _____		

Chapter VIII

PITFALLS

POTENTIAL planning pitfalls and opportunities are listed in this chapter.

1. A major error often made in planning hospitals is failure to think big enough. Almost always there is a shortage of funds. The pressure usually is "on" to conserve space tightly and to restrict planning. This may lead into more serious difficulty than taking the opposite approach and encourage planners to raise their sights and express fully their viewpoints.

2. Of growing importance is the question of interior design. Chapter VI is devoted to this subject as it represents a relatively new concept in hospital planning. The need for specialized interior design assistance has evolved as a result of the greater degree of attention people everywhere are according their surroundings. Coupled with this is the very rapid development of materials used in furnishings and in equipment which prolong the useful life of these assets and may contribute to lower operating costs. As this represents a large market and one that is difficult to keep pace with, a specialist is needed. Also, while the architect is concerned with the color and texture of walls, floors and ceiling . . . unless the draperies, furniture finishes and fabrics are coordinated carefully with the structure, the final result will fall far short of being as pleasant an environment as it might well be. Professional fees of a competent designer should be recovered by more economical purchases and longer life of furnishings.

3. When the committee has been organized and its professional advisors retained, objectives need to be defined, usually by the technical experts but subject to careful evaluation by the committee. Few projects are planned without developing differences

[47]

of *opinion* regarding the allocation of space and funds. Here experts earn their compensation. They should develop sufficient *facts* to enable the committee to reach an effective decision.

Careful attention to color, texture and lighting makes it possible to create a warm inviting environment and yet hold operating costs to a minimum.

It may be far better to get all requests and ideas on the conference table from the beginning. This does not imply that everything desired by the most ambitious department will be built, or certainly not built at any one time. However, it is virtually impossible to add essential components to a building later unless they have been anticipated. If the stress on economy is tight, the need for future elevators may not be revealed. Yet it would cost very little to design and construct the building with extra empty elevator shafts. Laboratories have been growing at a rate in excess of 10 per cent per year. Unless this is recognized, the laboratory may be obsolete before the paint is dry.

4. One fundamental problem many hospitals must face is

whether to expand and remodel an existing plant as opposed to building a completely new structure. The dilemma of many planners is that the investment in the old plant is so heavy, and so little may be recovered should it be discarded, the funds required to build new from the ground up may seem to be unattainable. This is the basic reason so many hospitals become a series of wings and pieces of seemingly unrelated buildings attached here and there to meet the crisis of the moment with insufficient regard for the total relationship and with none for the future. This also is the reason, in many instances, why hospital care costs so much. The very structure itself prohibits providing quality care in an efficient economical manner.

5. An entirely new, well-designed, modern plant with the best time-saving equipment and lowest maintenance costs can be operated for as much as 15 per cent less than a comparable size hospital handicapped by old, obsolete and inadequate structures with less than the best equipment. Today a well-managed hospital can borrow the capital it needs to support new plant and equipment . . . and liquidate the indebtedness from the money saved in lower cost by a more efficient structure. An old building, until recently a drag on the market, may now have an extended life as a nursing home or convalescent hospital. It might be possible to sell the old hospital to serve this purpose and provide some capital toward financing the new plant and equipment.

6. Planners may want to seek major economies that could result from much closer working relationship with other hospitals. It may be possible to construct certain centralized facilities. Many institutions now are involved in a central laundry operation, to their satisfaction at lower initial cost and with significant operating economies. Equally attractive opportunities are present in direct patient care services. One institution may specialize in the development of a particular specialized service while leaving a different, comparable service to be conducted by a cooperating hospital. Mergers of entire institutions are no longer uncommon. In the interest of quality and economy of care, immediate and in the long-term future, opportunities of this nature need to be given serious consideration by hospital planners.

7. Not until the total concept for expansion and remodeling has been expressed can the architect really begin to develop the format for the structure. Some architects wisely insist on converting the concepts to written form and obtaining agreement before beginning the drafting stage. There is much to be said for this approach. Cost *estimates* take on real meaning at this point and serve as a guide to the finance committee and governing board in ascertaining the possibilities for funding the project in whole or in part.

8. It is most important that the committee establish a definite schedule with objectives and dates determined as closely as possible. It is equally important that the committee recognize the value of consistent communication with all elements of the organization. Every step forward from schematics to preliminary, working and final drawings should be presented carefully.

9. The chief executive officer may want to establish a checklist of the type found in Chapter VII, page 44, so that he can pinpoint assignments made to management people and follow their progress throughout the project.

Chapter IX

EQUIPMENT

MAKING decisions regarding the selection of equipment is every bit as difficult as sorting out the opportunities offered in building design and arriving at the most optimum solution. While no one answer can apply to all situations, several guidelines may be helpful.

Hospital suppliers offer a contract under which the supplier will accept total responsibility for equipping the unit under consideration. They will do so at a reasonable figure and the owners will have a degree of latitude in exercising their preferences for specific items. This can almost be a "turnkey" arrangement with all supplies and equipment in place at the appointed time.

On the other hand, a well-managed organization with a competent purchasing staff might accomplish the same assignment at a lower cost and with fewer limitations in selection. Turning the assignment over to one supplier can create ill will among local dealers.

If the hospital is going to assume full responsibility for selection and purchase of equipment and supplies, the decision should be made at the outset that this will be accomplished primarily on a bid basis, using detailed specifications. Whenever possible, the specifications should be written to include the products of at least two competing *manufacturers* and the services of at least two competing *distributors*. Having distributor compete against distributor may not be sufficient to achieve the lowest cost for quality items. Institutions require first quality equipment. Anything less seldom stands the test of hard wear and long life.

For major items of equipment, it is most advisable to request manufacturers to place their items on display alongside their competitors at a location convenient to the hospital for sufficient time to allow careful inspection and comparison by interested parties. Before a final decision is reached on a bed, or other high-cost piece of equipment, the responsible hospital official should make a check of an adequate sample of present owners of the beds to be certain they have been satisfied with their decision in terms of performance. If it is possible to purchase the beds most likely to be selected and to place them in use for sufficient time to permit evaluation, this is an excellent method to follow.

An alternative to this approach is to take advantage of the annual meeting of the American Hospital Association and to inspect the wares of the manufacturers which are on full display, and where comparisons can be made.

If the hospital has been in existence it is highly desirable to call upon the accumulated experience of present personnel to assist in decisions where their competence is greatest. This can be done in two dimensions; identifying items needed as well as suggesting specific articles which have functioned best in use. This is most advisable with items used by physicians. Unless surgeons have an opportunity to express their preference regarding operating room lights and comparable equipment, the possibilities are very great indeed that the light purchased will be wrong. There is every reason to call upon the surgeon to participate in this decision. True, surgeons themselves may have difficulty in coming to a decision, but once made, with their participation, they will stand behind the selection when the light has been installed and is in use.

A comparable opportunity is available in the identification and selection of the infinite number of items used by nurses, food service people, technicians and others working in many specialized fields that make up the hospital. Housekeeping and maintenance personnel might well be brought into decisions that relate to the probable life and cost of upkeep. Typical factors to consider are illustrated here with fabric. Material recommended by interior designers could be cleaned by the hospital before installation in same manner that it would have to be cleaned during use to determine whether or not it will stand up well in the hospital environment. Will it resist soil? Shrink? Fade?

Withstand repeated cleaning? Clean well with existing hospital equipment? Clean easily with minimum time and maximum use of labor-saving equipment? Will the manufacturer continue to supply the item when future replacement is required or should surplus stock be purchased for replacement purposes as wear takes its toll?

The United States Public Health Service has available suggested equipment and supply lists which can serve as a very useful guide to the hospital in terms of reducing the possibility of overlooking items which might be discovered only after the building was placed into use. Acquisition could then be difficult in the quantity and quality needed at the lowest price. If one key hospital official is charged with the responsibility for all acquisition, there wil be less possibility of omission. This is not to suggest one person make all decisions, but rather that he be responsible for seeing that all decisions are made.

It is quite essential that a realistic equipment budget be prepared early in the planning stage so that this cost factor can be built into the total financial structure. Suppliers can be very helpful in helping accomplish this objective as long as it is recognized that the purpose is to obtain guidelines and not a hard, fast, final unchangeable total sum. A factor easily overlooked in making budget estimate for supplies is the need to stock extensively those places of storage which are separated from the main supply area. Many articles must be stocked in central stores, as well as on the shelves of each nursing unit and perhaps at the bedside as in the case of water carafes, bedpans, and the like. Whereas equipment such as the number of beds can be determined accurately, an estimate must suffice in many instances for supplies. Providing 15 per cent to 20 per cent extra to stock shelves and pipelines may be desirable when the supply budget is assembled.

Some equipment determinations run in tandem with building design considerations. The type of equipment acquired for the food service department is contingent upon resolution of the question of central versus decentralized food preparation and distribution. The size and scope of service to be provided by central sterile supply is likewise dependent upon the number and design of the operating rooms and the estimated volume and mix of operations.

The number, size, design and mixture of vertical transportation equipment poses a difficult question, but, fortunately, the manufacturers in this field have developed realiable guides. A factor coming into play in this area is the escalator. A pair of well-located escalators between the ground floor and the first level in a building with most services on two lower floors may obviate the need for one or more elevators. (One major hospital made escalators the primary method of vertical transportation and supplemented escalators with elevators). Automatic unloading dumbwaiters for supply services have become standard. For high-rise buildings, high-speed elevators have demonstrated their value in relatively small added cost over low-speed equipment.

One word of caution needs to be stated regarding the recommendations of equipment manufacturers in some highly competitive fields. Eager sales representatives may have a tendency to claim exceptionally high output for their equipment so that it will compare most favorably with their competitors. The output claimed may be possible under the most ideal conditions, but seldom achieved in terms of actual day-to-day use in the hospital. Unless the hospital is aware of this factor, usually not pointed up by the manufacturers, the twist ending to the installation may be that the department in question actually is *undersold* and underequipped . . . and even trapped in too small a space with little opportunity for correction except at great expense and considerable difficulty.

Hospital consultants often are able to help resolve these questions as they are able to draw upon multiple experiences in coping with the same problem in numerous hospitals involving many manufacturers and are well informed on current trends.

Chapter X

STAFFING

ONE of the most difficult questions to resolve is the number, quality and classification of employees required to provide the quality of care determined upon. The question of the level of care itself is perplexing because there are so few objective reliable measurements. To oversimplify the case, it is relatively simple to determine whether to purchase manual or electric typewriters and to ascertain the number needed based on requirements. But how is the performance of a nursing unit to be determined and how is the quality of food service or the clarity of an x-ray film objectively ascertained? Is the objective of the hospital to meet the *needs* of the patient as determined by the doctor and nurse or is it to meet the *desires* of the patient as he sees them? There may be a considerable difference between these two viewpoints and there may be a considerable difference between individual viewpoints of the professional staff as well as between viewpoints of individual patients.

The problem of allocating resources enters into staffing determinations, particularly when skilled people are in short supply. Will the available RNs be assigned in greater numbers to the obstetrical service?

STAFFING STANDARDS

Fortunately some inroad has been made into this complex question by a large number of California hospitals who are organized into a cooperative not-for-profit-corporation, the Commission for Administrative Services to Hospitals. More than 125 hospitals, large and small, government, nonprofit and proprietary, in cities and in rural areas, have employed jointly a team of competent industrial engineers to study objectively each department within the hospital to measure output and then to establish staffing standards. In nursing, each component of patient care has been observed frequently in a wide variety of situations within hospitals of many different types to enable a reliable standard time to be determined. When this effort was initiated, the response was that every patient is different, which he is, and that therefore it was impossible to set a standard time. The C.A.S.H. industrial engineers, accustomed to hearing this, patiently and carefully were able to relate comparable problems in other fields which have been solved. The insurance actuary is faced with the question of supplying the underwriter with a standard table of life expectancy which can be applied to each policyholder, despite all the variations between individuals.

Once reliable standard times were established, the next step was to ascertain what each hospital desired to provide as its level of service to its patients. How many medications, baths, pulse, temperature and respirations per patient per day? Again, the objection was raised that patients vary in their needs. However it eventually was realized that if nothing else, a maximum determination could be set beyond which no patient would need care. Coupling standard time factors to the type and frequency of nursing care procedures deemed advisable for patients enabled C. A. S. H. experts to accurately determine the number of hours of nursing care per patient per day and the proper "mix" of skills needed to meet the required number of hours.

QUALITY CONTROL

Going further, a method to measure objectively the quality of performance of nursing personnel then was developed. That is, a form of quality control was devised, and is being used successfully by scores of California hospitals. The plan is to have quality control teams of nurses make rounds of patient units other than the one they are assigned to and to list their observations on a standardized record. The type of observation recorded varies with respect to the nature of the patient's illness. An example of the guide used on a surgical nursing unit may be seen on page 60.

The standard number of hours of care per patient per day now used as a guide by the majority of hospitals participating in the California cooperative program follows.

Type of Nursing Unit	Standard Hours of Care Per Patient Per Day
Adult medical and surgical patients	4.0
Pediatrics	5.33
Nursery	3.16
Obstetrical	3.40
Psychiatric	2.56
Intensive Surgical Care	13.54
Intensive Medical Care	7.33

The Commission for Administrative Services to Hospitals continued the establishment of staffing patterns for other departments of the hospital including the following:

Department	Standard
Food Service	.90
Housekeeping	.80
Business Office	.50
Laboratory	(Not Available)
X-ray	(Not Available)
Medical Records	(Not Available)

It is unnecessary to caution that these figures may not apply equally well in every hospital due to the lack of standardization of design and equipment, differences in the capabilities of personnel and in the expectation of patients in various regions. Nevertheless, a hospital can arrive at a rather accurate forecast by comparing its current staffing with C.A.S.H. standards and then projecting future requirements based upon these two known quantities. The entirely new hospital building from the ground up can place considerable reliance upon the standards in forecasting its personnel requirements and payroll costs.

One factor calling for independent judgment based upon local circumstances is whether or not to overstaff a unit in its initial phase of operation. Every building contains some deficiencies which will become known only when subject to the test and stress of daily use. If an immediate surge in occupancy is anticipated, thought should be given to initial staffing at a somewhat higher level than normal in order to provide the quality of service desired while "bugs" are being worked out. Normal attrition soon will bring the staff down to the predetermined level deemed necessary for regular conditions.

PREOPENING PERSONNEL

Depending upon the nature and extent of the program, certain key people will need to be employed well in advance of opening day. On an entirely new project, the chief executive officer should be selected and employed at the earliest possible moment. If the selection is sound, this individual will be in a key position to be helpful throughout planning, construction, equipping, staffing, initial operation and on to the next phase of growth. If he is on the job and able to participate in the selection of the architect, consultant, engineers, and interior designers, the entire project will proceed in the best possible manner. When the top operating executive arrives late, he has had no opportunity to contribute to the early stages and he may have difficulty in accepting as his own and giving unquestioned support to every aspect of the program. A smooth-running, coordinated team with a competent chief executive officer heading the staff from the beginning should expedite planning and should reduce costs well beyond the expense of having leadership skill on hand in this position.

A purchasing agent can more than earn his way in a project of any size. In a small hospital without the service of a specialist in this activity, an expansion program might signal the proper time for employing such a person. Exactly the same observation can be made with regard to a personnel director. Employment of the head of nursing, pharmacy, food service and the other major departments cannot long be delayed without facing penalties in terms of patient care. Contracts with medical specialist for x-ray, laboratory and other comparable departments need to be established while the building is in the design stage, if at all possible. A laboratory designed by competent architects supported by able consultants in a hospital directed by an experienced chief executive was obsolete the day a top-quality pathologist walked in. Within months from opening day, a new greatly-expanded laboratory was on the drafting board. Extensive and expensive changes were required which could have been avoided if the pathologist had been selected while the original project was in the design stage.

MEDICAL STAFF

Although the scope of this book does not include medical staff organization and activity, and it is widely recognized that physicians should be encouraged to participate in planning, the point is worth stressing. Six months after a 200-bed general hospital with an adjacent 100-bed convalescent unit was placed into use, the governing board called in a team of hospital consultants to determine why the occupancy had not exceeded seventeen patients. The hospital was in a rapidly growing metropolitan area. There was an acute shortage of beds in a famed medical center complex just a few miles distant from the virtually empty new hospital which was validating its nonprofit status with a loss exceeding $70,000 per month.

The single biggest mistake the planners made was to not involve actively, consult with and seek the support of local practicing physicians, elementary as this may seem to be. This is not simply a matter of writing a letter or calling upon a physician to advise him that a new hospital is going to be built and asking if he would care to use it. Most doctors are pleased to see more beds available in their community and would so express themselves on inquiry. But each active attending physician has had to work out a satisfactory method of practice, including the use of a hospital. Seldom will he switch allegiance and disrupt his pattern of practice simply because someone is making more beds available. To be meaningful, his involvement ordinarily would have to be much deeper and the reasons for using the new hospital much more significant.

Additionally, doctors have experience with a wide variety of hospital designs as they complete their education. They may have accumulated many helpful ideas, based upon first-hand experience, which would contribute toward the best possible design.

QUALITY CONTROL CHECK SHEET
MEDICAL/SURGICAL

Floor_____Unit_____Room_____Date_____Time_____

Patient_____By_____

Diagnosis_____Age_____Date Admitted_____

A. PATIENT WELFARE AND SAFETY

	Yes	No
1. Patient does not appear to require immediate attention.		
2. Patient's attitude towards his care appears satisfactory?		
3. Side rails up if required?		
4. Call light within easy reach and working?		
5. Patient's skin condition satisfactory?		
6. Dressing clean and comfortable?		
7. Equipment, tube, etc. functioning?		
8. Nursing performing procedure correctly and efficiently?		
Totals		

B. PATIENT COMFORT AND ACCESSIBILITY OF IMMEDIATE NEEDS

	Yes	No
1. Patient appears to be comfortable?		
2. Bed neatly made and comfortably positioned?		
3. Urinal empty, rinsed, cover on and positioned?		
4. Bed pan empty, rinsed, cover on and positioned?		
5. Bedside table and personal effects within easy reach?		
6. Before meal—patient prepared?		
7. After meal—finished tray removed?		
Totals		

C. PATIENT ROOM

	Yes	No
1. Room appearance satisfactory?		
2. Closet orderly and stocked?		
3. Lavatory orderly, clean, stocked?		
4. Noise level satisfactory to the patient?		
5. Lighting satisfactory to patient?		
6. Temperature and ventilation satisfactory to patient?		
Totals		

Observer's Comments (Reference Number)

Chapter XI

TEST RUN

THE concept of a test run has merit when adapted to the hospital before a new unit is placed in full-scale use. Most building projects take so long to complete everyone is anxious to conduct opening ceremonies and accept the first patients. The end often sees a scurry of activity by many craftsmen finishing painting, laying floor covering, installing cover on electrical fixtures, and, on the outside, gardeners work to get plantings in place and parking lots marked off with dividing lines.

CLEAN-UP

There is a tremendous amount of clean-up work. This can pose a delicate problem as most hospital employees are not unionized while virtually all construction crews are composed of union members. The building construction contract may call for a clean structure . . . but there is a vast difference between the hospital standard of cleanliness and that of most construction crews. Before accepting patients, the hospital undoubtedly will want to give every corner a good final cleaning. Time must be allowed for this, and to avoid possible conflict with unions it may be desired to wait until the structure is accepted from the contractor and his crew is gone.

RECEIVING, INSPECTING AND PLACING EQUIPMENT

Also to be reckoned with is the very extensive job of tagging carefully each piece of incoming equipment and supply crate and carton; checking against purchase orders; inspecting for possible damage and being certain all specifications have been met.

As storage space is at a premium, the majority of equipment and supplies probably will be scheduled for arrival during a short span just prior to opening. Consequently, there will be a heavy demand in time and effort to meet this need; getting the items assembled and in their proper places is no easy assignment.

Depending upon the locale, it may be advisable to employ armed security guards around the clock just to safeguard supplies and equipment during this hectic period and during public open house if one is scheduled. Thieves at one hospital took five thousand dollars worth of linen and three wall-mounted TV sets from patient rooms.

BREAK-IN PERIOD

Every department of the new unit should have a full-scale test run of all equipment for a sufficiently long period to detect faulty installations, missing items and inoperable or malfunctioning gear. It just isn't possible to build a major structure, equip and supply it without running into unforeseen problems. Sections of ceilings falling due to a missed drain connection pouring gallons of water into the crawl space between ceiling and floor . . . or electrical outlets for vital equipment arriving with three-prong electrical connections while the wall outlet provides a two-prong receptacle . . . elevators leveling three inches above or below the floor level . . . nurse-patient intercom being wired so that it is impossible to determine from what room a call originates . . . telephone connections mixed up . . . these are all typical of confusion surrounding final stages of the project. Similar problems should be anticipated.

EMPLOYEE ORIENTATION

Employees, whether they are old reliable workers or newly hired may have difficulty becoming oriented to a new environment where there is any significant degree of change from their accustomed situation. Unless they are provided ample opportunity to function in advance of the day the first patient arrives, each task they undertake doubtlessly will require added time and effort. In some instances, opening day has been the occasion for patients arriving at 5:00 P. M. for admission but nurses not arriving on the nursing station until 10:30 P. M.; hamburgers being served in place of the regular menu and patients being "lost" for a day or two within the hospital as admitting records and identification tags were mixed.

A number of services can have full-scale trial runs: Food service can prepare meals for working crews; the laundry can process newly received linen; central sterile supply can do likewise with items it handles; diagnostic and therapeutic departments can offer "free" procedures to volunteers. Volunteers may be willing to act as "patients" for a day, going through the entire admitting process and actually occupying a bed to give nursing personnel and opportunity to work with simulated patients. Food, housekeeping and other services can get the "feel" of the new unit at the same time.

Every precaution taken before the first patient is accepted will reduce unexpected problems and help to make the period following opening a relatively smooth-running operation. Word will spread throughout the community that "the hospital really is wonderful and everyone seems to know exactly what his job is." If there is confusion, delay, untoward events, and breakdowns, people become apprehensive. It may take a long time to recover from such avoidable setbacks; occupancy may be slow to build up. A lag in income during the time when staffing is heavy and many nonrecurring expenses take place may throw the hospital into a serious deficit position which could hamper it for a long time to come.

Chapter XII

PUBLIC ACCEPTANCE

EXPANSION and remodeling provide the hospital with an excellent opportunity to build and enhance public acceptance. People are stimulated by progress within their community. Many welcome having a chance to understand the hospital better. Groundbreaking, cornerstone-laying and dedication ceremonies along with open-house tours can be developed into excellent public-education programs involving personal participation by large numbers of people.

GOLDEN OPPORTUNITY

The hospital does not exist that could not benefit from greater public understanding, acceptance and support. Once erected, equipped and staffed, the effort and investment necessary to gain a full measure of acceptance should not be spared. The nature of hospitals is such that they can function effectively only when well staffed; consequently the fixed-cost proportion of their operating costs is very high in relation to total operating costs. A relatively high level of occupancy is required to meet the heavy fixed costs. The better the public knows and accepts the hospital, the more likely it is that use will be adequate to generate income sufficient to cover operating costs.

In regard to occupancy, it is correct that, except for those who decide personally to use the emergency service, hardly a patient reaches the hospital who has not been directed there by a physician. Further, this is not to suggest that a "Madison Avenue" advertising approach be conducted to build unnecessary use of the hospital. However, there are times when the doctor wants a patient to go to the hospital that he runs into a wall of resistance which may be traced back to a long-standing fear of hospitals, which is a carryover from the very early history of these institutions. Some people vaguely recall that more patients used to die in hospitals than recovered and that hospitals were the place patients suffering from communicable disease were isolated. Gaining knowledge and confidence in the local community hospital by being made fully aware of progressive new construction and the acquisition of the newest and best equipment can helpfully reassure and prepare people for the day when the doctor says, "I'm going to send you to the hospital."

Additionally, if the hospital is eligible for donations and contributions, people need to be made fully aware of the hospital, of its needs, and of the desirability of helping to support this essential community health facility. Successfully completed construction programs, when well presented, provide an excellent peg upon which to hang news stories in the press and on radio and television. More people are making greater contributions to eleemosynary institutions than ever before in history, but they, of course, give financial support only to the organization with which they are most familiar, have confidence in, and are motivated to assist.

STEPLADDER TO SUCCESS

It is very desirable to assign one knowledgeable person to the task of achieving maximum public acceptance for the hospital, and particularly so during a major expansion and remodeling effort. Each forward step can be reported to the public:

The initial decision to build;
Selection of a building committee;
Selection of architect, consultant, engineers, interior designers;
Preliminary sketches of the proposed structure;
Plans and specification out to bid;
Award of the contract;
Groundbreaking;
Construction progress at various times;
Award of key equipment contracts;
Appointment of key hospital workers;

Cornerstone ceremony;

Announcement of dedication plans;

Dedication program;

Public tours;

Distinguished visitors, and

Reports of new activities.

INFORMATION IN DEPTH

Best results are obtained if the "public" is grouped into the immediate hospital "family" and into the public at large. Depending upon the number of people in the "family" it may be advisable to recognize the distinction between doctors, volunteers and employees. Whenever possible, the "family" should have the benefit of receiving news before it is circulated in the public media.

An internal newsletter written and addressed to the medical staff can be very hepful if prepared on a monthly basis. Doctors are expected by their patients to have inside advance information about the hospital. A brief factual multilith or mimeographed news release containing essentially the same information prepared for general circulation but mailed to members of the medical staff a few days in advance will be appreciated by most physicians. The same approach taken with volunteers and employees will be productive of good will. Each such bulletin should be written to meet the special interest of the group to which it is addressed. Doctors will be much more interested in detailed information about the layout of the surgical and delivery suites than would the volunteer or average employee.

General news media need to have a substantial lead item in order to justify carrying a story . . . first; biggest; newest; most; only; dollar amounts; miles of electric wire; tons of cement . . . these are the types of facts that find their way into the opening paragraph of news stories, feature columns, and into the radio and TV personality shows.

Dedication is worthy of special attention as a major event in the life cycle of the hospital. Planning might well begin a year prior to the anticipated day of dedication. Possibilities to be evaluated include the following:

Special edition of the local paper financed with advertisements from contractors and suppliers;

Interviews arranged on radio and TV. Board president, chief of staff, director of nurses, dietitian, volunteer president . . . all offer opportunities, if skillfully presented well in advance;

Special commemorative brochure reporting key historical facts, highlights of the current program and a look into the future;

Invitations to local service clubs to hold their weekly or monthly meetings at the hospital during dedication period; Special invitation to public and private school officials to have prescheduled tours for teachers and for students;

Elementary students often tour the fire station and would tour the hospital if properly arranged. Junior and senior high school students might be particularly interested in a visit to the clinical laboratories;

Special invitations to the clergy, barbers, taxi drivers to schedule a tour at a time of their particular convenience;

Preview for medical staff members, wives and families;

Preview for volunteers and their families;

Preview for employees and their families;

Preview for press, radio and TV. Hand out complete file of facts, key people, provide photo coverage;

Schedule the dedication program so that it is presented as a smooth-running production, carefully timed and with effective public speakers. Have a section reserved for special people. Distribute printed programs. Use an attention-gathering method to symbolize the official opening. The cry of a new-born infant activating an electromechanical door opener, as contrasted with the customary ribbon cutting, will produce more press coverage;

Follow up stories on the first admission, first baby born, first patient discharged . . . all offer excellent news "pegs."

If the same size and scope of project were undertaken by a department store or industrial firm and the equivalent need existed to sell a new product, the effort likely would be supported by a carefully thought-out and well-conducted campaign. Hospitals cannot advertise as this would be considered unethical for sound, long-standing reasons. Yet the need to acquaint the public with the hospital is just as great and the task is somewhat more difficult with advertising ruled out. A skillfully planned and conducted program of the nature described will return an excellent reponse in better understanding, more widespread acceptance and greater support for the hospital.

Chapter XIII

FINANCING EXPANSION

MOST communities will need to invest up to $100 per man, woman and child for general hospital expansion between 1965 and 1980. This is in addition to another $100 per person which may be needed for mental and long-term hospitals. To place this sum in its proper perspective, consider that it cost approximately $2.50 per person for the United States to send the first astronaut into space. The $400 million required for this space age project represents only a small fraction of the sum needed for hospital expansion and construction across the nation.

NEED FOR FUNDS

Here we will stress the magnitude of the need for funds, pinpoint the responsibility, outline sources and methods used to help solve this major problem.

To determine the magnitude of local responsibility, locate the position of your community on the following table:

CAPITAL NEEDS FOR GENERAL HOSPITAL EXPANSION 1965-80

POPULATION	CAPITAL NEEDS
1,000	$ 100,000.00
5,000	$ 500,000.00
10,000	$ 1,000,000.00
20,000	$ 2,000,000.00
40,000	$ 4,000,000.00
100,000	$10,000,000.00
200,000	$20,000,000.00

If the population of your town is 1,000 people, $100,000 will be needed for hospital expansion in the next fifteen years; if the population of your community is 5,000 persons, you will need $500,000; if 20,000 persons, the demand will be for $2 million, and proportionally higher if your city is larger.

These are not rough estimates. They are realistic indications of needed hospital and medical construction assembled from surveys made by the federal government.

The sum required may be staggering; many communities must obtain a great deal of capital if they are to meet the local hospital needs of the people in the years immediately ahead.

You may ask, "Why is this the case?"

1. *Expansion* need traced to normal growth in population; aging of population; developments stemming from medical research; migration, and health insurance, including "medicare."

2. *Modernization* demanded by: the need to eliminate unsafe buildings, the need for more effective utilization of facilities and of skilled workers and the need to provide new diagnostic and therapeutic services.

Another way of stating the general situation is to say that there needs to be as much new capital invested in hospitals between 1965-1980 as now is represented by the total existing assets of *all* hospitals.

SOURCES

How will these needs be met? Particularly in light of competition for funds from schools and churches, from governmental agencies for streets, sewers, and courthouses, from utilities for water, electricity, and gas? The most commonly used sources of capital funds for hospitals are listed below.

1. Operating income.	6. Government grants.
2. Fund drives.	7. Foundations.
3. Bequests.	8. Bond issue.
4. Loans.	9. Deferred payments.
5. Investments.	

Every possible source needs to be studied, evaluated and utilized as the local situation warrants. It is probable, of course, that several will be selected to finance expansion as hospitals typically rely on more than one source for their capital fund requirements. Duke University Medical Center has made available results of a survey of methods of securing capital funds by 143 hospitals. The following chart shows their findings.

Hill Burton	Long-term Borrowing by Hospital	Bonded Indebtedness by Taxing Agency	Private Contributions	Hospital Reserves	Other	Total
1. $47,258. (19.3%)	55,187. (22.6%)	33,379. (13.7%)	69,373. (28.4%)	22,575. (9.3%)	16,311. (6.7%)	244,083. (100%)
2. $38,677. (18.8%)	38,006. (18.5%)	29,335. (14.3%)	67,168. (32.7%)	21,248. (10.4%)	10,822. (5.3%)	205,256. (100%)
3. $ 8,581. (22.1%)	17,181. (44.2%)	4,044. (10.4%)	2,205. (5.7%)	1,327. (3.4%)	5,489. (14.2%)	38,827. (100%)
4. $30,484. (19.2%)	33,249. (21.0%)	5,110. (3.2%)	64,359. (40.7%)	17,597. (11.1%)	7,517. (4.8%)	158,316. (100%)
4a. $ 5,624. (16.8%)	12,743. (38.0%)	–0–	10,660. (31.8%)	4,065. (12.2%)	420. (1.2%)	33,512. (100%)
4b. $24,860. (19.9%)	20,506. (16.4%)	5,110. (4.1%)	53,698. (43.0%)	13,532. (10.8%)	7,098. (5.8%)	124,804. (100%)
5. $ 8,193. (23.4%)	2,832. (8.1%)	19,925. (56.9%)	307. (.9%)	2,398. (6.8%)	1,371. (3.9%)	35,026. (100%)

1. Total reported construction costs of all reporting institutions (143).

2. Reported construction costs of hospitals registered with the American Hospital Association on August 1, 1965 (110).

3. Reported construction costs of nonregistered institutions (33).

4. Reported construction costs of voluntary nonprofit hospitals registered with the American Hospital Association (78).

4a. Reported construction costs of church-related or operated hospitals registered with the American Hospital Association (20).

4b. Reported construction costs of other nonprofit hospitals registered with the American Hospital Association (58).

5. Reported construction costs of governmental, nonfederal hospitals registered with the American Hospital Association (27).

It is not enough, however, to know the sources of income and the degree to which each is being relied on to provide capital funds for hospitals. It is equally important to become acquainted intimately with these money markets. But the average hospital doesn't often "Come to the well," as they say on Wall Street. Trustees, doctors, and hospital executives usually do not know the hospital money market. In my personal experience working to obtain well over $20,000,000 for various hospital projects, I learned the importance of relying heavily on experts to reduce the cost, save time and effort, and to get the money!

VOLUNTARY FUND DRIVES

W. D. "Bob" Curry, vice president of American City Bureau/Beaver, Inc., who has successfully guided hospitals through close to $40,000,000 of voluntary capital financing, outlines seven factors as basic to success in fund raising.

1. *Convincing Evidence.* There must be a clearly defined need for the facilities which the building fund will make possible. There must be convincing evidence that, until the need is met, the hospital, its physicians and its patients, will be handicapped by lack of adequate facilities for health protection. Furthermore, the program must fit into a carefully-planned, long-range community health picture.

2. *Must Measure Up.* The hospital must measure the status of its relationship with the people it serves, and plan a consistent effort to promote sound relations. The hospital must undertake a program of pre-campaign preparation and education and also the correction of certain conditions, if factors warrant such action.

3. *No Other Alternatives.* It must be shown that the plan proposed to meet the end actually will meet it and is possible of fulfillment. Compelling evidence should be presented that there are no alternatives to a fund-raising campaign that hold equal promise of success in solving the problem. It should be possible to prove the need for a campaign to the satisfaction of any unbiased person. All reasonable alternatives to the fundraising campaign must have been fully explored and found to be less satisfactory.

4. *Dedicated and Confidence Inspiring.* The hospital's governing board must be a representative and confidence-inspiring group. In addition, the board must be united in its support of the program before it asks for public support. If the hospital's appeal is not strong enough to win the enthusiastic endorsement of its board, it hardly can win the favorable consideration of persons who are acquainted less intimately with the hospital. Not only moral but financial support is required from members of the board. Eventually the scale of contributions set by them will determine the scale of giving to be followed by the community as a whole. Potential subscribers will wish to know what other persons of the same means are giving, and they will scale their contributions up or down accordingly.

5. *Competent Hospital Administrator.* The fifth must, before undertaking a fund-raising campaign, is the insurance of competent hospital administration. Sometimes a good board is handicapped in its appeal for funds because the quality of its administration is not as high as the community has a right to expect. This is less likely to be true today than it was in the past because most governing boards realize that the task of administering a hospital is one that calls for special abilities and trained judgment. Today most men and women who enter hospital administration do so only after extensive preparation, either through a graduate course in hospital administration, or through a long apprenticeship to a competent administrator.

6. *Medical Staff Democratically Organized.* The sixth must is that the medical staff be of high standing and organized democratically. Its staff should grant privileges to all doctors in strict accordance with their competence and integrity, and should be representative of the younger, as well as the older physicians. Obviously, in a metropolitan community, every hospital cannot have on its staff all the men of outstanding reputation in that city. But unless a hospital has a fair proportion of the really good physicians, it is not in a strong position to appeal to the public. And, medical interest and giving to the project is an index to the need.

7. *Appropriate Timing.* Finally, the effort must be timed appropriately in view of other community projects and needs.

HOSPITAL BOND ISSUES

Success factors in obtaining voter support for public bond issues have been defined by Harry Frishman of the Long Beach Unified School District, who has guided campaigns producing close to $100,000,000. Mr. Frishman stressed the importance of proper planning well in advance of the public vote on the issue. He emphasized the importance of appealing to the *emotions* of the citizens in terms they can accept.

Do not ask the citizens to vote money for hospitals, but do obtain their help in bringing modern medical miracles within the reach of all people of the community. Don't gamble with the life of your boy or girl—your loved ones.

Reasons not to utilize the bond issuse must be anticipated and answered satisfactorily for all opponents before the major public effort is launched.

A complete and exhaustive effort is required during the last month of the campaign, but success will solve not only the immediate capital funds problems—it will make all subsequent hospital obectives easier to accomplish after two-thirds or more of the people vote "Yes" for the Hospital Bond issue.

Nine basic guidelines for successful bond issue campaigns follow:

1. It is not so much *what* you do, but how you do it that counts.

2. There isn't any easy way—it's hard work.

3. Newspapers can't win for you, but they can defeat you.

4. Involve great numbers of people; what a friend says is important.

5. Emotion is more valuable than reason.

6. Don't stress the negative—avoid debates and negative questions if possible.

7. Team a professional worker with a recognized civic leader on each committee.

8. Tell what the hospital does—not what it is.

9. One opponent can do more harm than 500 supporters can remedy.

LEASE PURCHASING

Deferred payment is another frequently used source of funds. American Hospital Supply Corporation President, Harry DeWitt, points out several big factors inherent to this method of hospital financing:

Consideration of the desirability of leasing equipment, as opposed to purchasing it outright, depends very largely on the purchaser's needs and on his financial condition. A hospital with very little money, faced with the prospect of equipping 100 beds, has a relatively limited choice. It can lease the equipment; it can borrow from one source or another the money to buy the equipment; or, if it can find a dealer, who will shoulder the risk without adding too great a surcharge to the normal cost of the equipment involved, it can make a minimal down payment and pay that dealer in installments over an agreed-upon period of years. A hospital with adequate funds also, might, under certain circumstances, deem it good business to preserve its liquid cash and either lease the equipment needed or borrow the money from any of the sources I have suggested.

I believe any hospital can evaluate the advantages and disadvantages of leasing only in comparison with other available methods of financing the acquisition of capital goods. It is entirely conceivable that leasing could be highly desirable from the standpoint of one hospital; highly undesirable for another hospital, even though its financial situation might be substantially the same.

BANK FINANCE MORTGAGE LOANS

The Bank of America has pinpointed, in detail, factors bankers consider in making long-term mortgage loans to hospitals. Experience indicates that seldom will such a loan exceed 20 to 30 per cent of the total cost of the project, or extend beyond a five to ten year period. Because the hospital structure is a "single-purpose" building and a "business" that no bank would want to foreclose, hospitals must pass very close examination.

In considering a loan, the bank will require:
1. Plans and specifications.
2. Cost breakdown.
3. Survey substantiating the need.
4. Resume of sponsors and management.
5. Listing of medical staff.
6. Audited financial statements for five years (if an existing hospital).
7. Detailed source of other capital.
8. Projection of income, expense and cash flow.
9. Financial statements of guarantors of loan.

In addition to these supporting documents, banks will consider carefully:
1. Management ability. Must be capable, experienced and free to formulate and carry out sound policies.
2. Location. Should be near center of community population and easily accessible. Adequate utilities and drainage. Maximum light and air, free from smoke and odors, adequate parking and ample room for expansion also are essential.
3. Official approval. Must have received official approval of State Department of Public Health.

INSURANCE COMPANY MORTGAGE LOANS

Although insurance companies do not seek out hospital loans, they sometimes will aid in financing. The hospital interested in obtaining an insurance company loan would be well advised to work through a leading local mortgage correspondent. Major factors considered by the loan correspondent and insurance company are as follows:
1. Need for the hospital project must be great.
2. Preferably a nonprofit community service institution of not less than 100 beds.
3. Chief Executive, as key to future success, is given the most careful study. Detailed resume required covering education, experience, background.
4. Must be complete facility, with laundry, food service, etc. with adequate parking, room for expansion.

5. Architect must have a record of past successful hospital experience and provide detailed plans, specifications, cost breakdowns.

6. Five years of audited statements, plus projection of income and expense.

7. Short sketch of Board of Trustees. Look for a well-balanced group of capable civic leaders.

8. Consideration given to medical staff and method of appointment.

9. Financial statement detailing all sources of capital.

10. Economic and physical appraisal of the property, utilizing an 80 per cent occupancy factor.

Terms of Insurance Company Loans:

1. Usually in range of 20-33$\frac{1}{3}$ per cent of value, or $3,500-$4,500 per bed on $18,000-$20,000 cost.

2. Chattel mortgage on all equipment is required.

3. Fifteen-year term.

4. Interest rate dependent upon market at time of application.

5. Deposit of 2 per cent of loan will accompany application.

6. Fees range from zero to 1 per cent of loan.

MORTGAGE LOAN UNDERWRITERS

For more than fifty years, the B. C. Ziegler Company of West Bend, Wisconsin has served nonprofit institutions as an investment banker and underwriter of hospital loans. Ziegler's president, D. J. Kenny, has pointed out that ample capital is available for sound projects provided:

If you are going to borrow money, do it wisely. Don't try to beat the law of compensation, the law of averages or the experience of history. Soundly conceived and developed projects may obtain loans up to 40 per cent of value when there is community demonstration of substantial local investment in the project. Underwriters require a five-year financial record reporting new earnings after depreciation and obsolescense at least equal to one and one-quarter times maximum annual interest charge on the proposed loan.

Experience over the years, indicates that for capital loans the most satisfactory amortization is a twenty-year level debt service with adequate pre-payment rights after five years. An initial eighteen-month "breathing spell" is desirable, as well as an "open-end" clause to permit further financing without disturbing the initial loan.

Standard terms of the mortgage, deed of trust or indenture include:

1. Meet the interest and principal installments as they come due.

2. Keep the property insured to the extent of 80 per cent of its reasonable insurable value, excluding uninsurables, and to carry other usual and customary forms of insurance.

3. Pay taxes, if any.

4. Keep the property in reasonable repair.

5. Remain solvent.

6. Keep sound accounts and annually provide a balance sheet and operating statement, preferably audited.

7. Agree not to dispose of property without receiving value.

8. Provide for modifications of the terms of the loan with the consent of the holders of two-thirds in principal amount of bonds or notes.

The normal cost of underwriting is equivalent to a charge of approxiately one-quarter of 1 per cent per annum. This covers initial services other than out-of-pocket costs, broker's fees, and also places the underwriter's expert financial counsel at the disposition of the hospital during the term of the loan.

Chapter XIV

LONG TERM FUND DEVELOPMENT

To achieve the optimum response in fund-raising efforts, hospitals have to tailor their appeals specifically to each of the various types of potential donors. Obtaining significant gifts from corporations calls for its own special approach. It is best to assume that the top management of a company will respond most favorably to a carefully worked-out presentation, which sets forth a specific need and documents the particular problem that must be solved in terms that are relevant to the corporation being approached. The presentation should set a definite dollar amount required to accomplish the job, and, if circumstances permit, indicate what similar companies have contributed.

By putting the request in the form of a report similar to those the company studies in the conduct of its normal business affairs, the appeal is placed in a frame of reference familiar to corporate officials. The more thorough and comprehensive the written presentation is, the more favorable will management's impression be concerning the effective use of the contribution being sought. A gift of consequence usually must be considered by more than one executive; frequently, a board of directors must act on it before funds can be released. If the company headquarters happens to be in a distant city, the request probably will have to be forwarded there for final action. This is another reason for presenting the proposal in the most concise and careful manner.

Some of the most successful long-term fund-raising efforts are centered around a simple, clear-cut, direct mail appeal. As a mailing list is carefully built, it grows in potential value, providing that a public relations program is also expanded to cultivate widespread interest in the work of the organization.

In using the mails for fund appeals, it is essential that the work of the organization is regarded as being important to society, that a reputation for effectiveness has been established, and that the widest possible audience is so informed. Unless all three elements are present, the direct mail appeal cannot be built upon a solid foundation, and other methods should be exploited.

A direct mail appeal may consist of nothing more than a carefully composed letter, or it may include both a letter and a specially prepared leaflet. In either case, an addressed return envelope should be enclosed. A recent study indicates that more gifts are received when the return envelope has free rather than stamped or franked postage.

The inside flap of the return envelope is a convenient place to restate in a few words the project(s) for which contributions are being requested. It may also be used for identification of the donor.

An immediate "thank you" letter should go to the donor. It is a good idea to again thank contributors at the end of the year and to list their names in the house organ or other publications. One of the important objectives of the direct-mail appeal is to contact the maximum number of potential givers with a minimum of effort. Although many contributions may be small, the fact that the person has considered the request and has responded favorably suggests that he may develop a habit of giving. This is a paramount factor, for the individual who has given small sums several times may well be the person who one day writes a bequest clause that includes your organization as the beneficiary.

GIFTS FROM OTHER AGENCIES

Hardly a community exists that is not organized into an amazing number of service clubs, work groups, PTA's, and religious, fraternal, and social groups. Increasingly, workers are forming in-plant groups, such as North American Aviation's, "Donate Once Club," to coordinate gift-giving within the company. Community Chests and United Fund groups are everywhere and charitable foundations number in the thousands. All have one thing in common of great interest to every hospital conducting a long-term fund-raising effort: they have assets at their disposition.

Although some of these groups may have a fixed long-term objective which calls for all the funds available, this is not usually the case. More often than not the officers and membership welcome an opportunity to extend their benevolences into new, worthwhile ventures in the community. The challenge here is much like that posed by a corporation, and for that reason, a well prepared presentation produces the best results. The appeal to this group is usually for assistance on smaller projects requiring fewer dollars and a stronger appeal to the emotions is appropriate in these instances.

In addition, a method that often appeals to service-oriented groups is a personal invitation to tour and inspect the premises. If it is possible to have a luncheon meeting on the site and to follow this with a presentation, the chances of a favorable response improve accordingly.

After receipt of a gift from this source, it is very important that follow-up action include community publicity and related forms of recognition. This is about the only reward that can be offered, and, if properly handled, it can cement relations for future requests. Reports made to the group from time to time, as the project might warrant, also serve to reinforce the appreciation that has already been expressed.

Whenever possible, it is desirable to tie the key leadership of these agencies closer to your organization in whatever ways can be evolved.

A contribution once received need not close the door to future requests for support. Changes of officers and members offer a problem, since the newcomers may not favor this disposition of funds, but these personnel changes also present an opportunity to stir fresh enthusiasm among new personalities.

AN ASSOCIATES GROUP

Colleges have scored major gains in fund development by establishing an "Associates of the College" group. Rice Institute in Houston, Texas, has an outstanding associates program. Membership calls for an annual payment to the institute of $10,000 per year. In return for this donation, the university keeps the contributor up to date on the results of various research programs under current investigation. This may or may not be of direct benefit to the contributor in the conduct of his business. But that does not matter, for the primary reason for the benefactor's annual gift is usually his belief that it is essential to the nation's well-being to keep the country's leading educational institutions free of governmental financial support and influence.

Huntington Library in Pasadena, California, has an organization known as "Friends of Huntington Library." Their purpose is to provide financial aid and develop wide community support for an outstanding facility which would seriously have to curtail its services without such assistance. Annual individual donations are kept modest, being just a few dollars a year.

Another approach is to go to the other end of the scale and appoint as an associate everyone who makes a donation during a calendar year. One hospital on the west coast has initiated this program, and the outlook is reported to be favorable.

There is no "best" way to establish an associates group, but there is considerable merit in having such an activity. Associates are an effective extension of the hospital and enable it to reach further into the community. Most likely, members would include all persons already connected with the hospital in a trustee or foundation capacity. This is a good core around which to develop the associates.

Others will affiliate with this type of loosely knit group which imposes little in the way of time-consuming responsibilities, whereas they might be unable or reluctant to assume a leadership position on the governing board. This arrangement is entirely feasible, workable, and desirable. The passing interest that comes from membership in the associates group might at some later date prove to be the beginning of a deeper concern and more active participation as a member of a policy-making board.

Programs for many such groups include regularly scheduled dinner meetings or conferences to which all associates in good standing are invited and at which a concise report is given spotlighting the affairs of the parent organization. Then, a physician or staff member presents an up-to-the-minute "insider" summary of a topic of general interest, which has not yet been released to the general public.

Associates may be given places of prominence when such public ceremonies as ground breaking or dedications of a new unit are being carried out. A roped-off, reserved-seat section is usually sufficient to create a feeling of importance for these friends and supporters. They would, of course, be included on most of the mailings originating from the organization. Occasionally, they might serve as "door openers" when important contacts with potential donors are being arranged.

One useful and rewarding device is issuing a certificate of appreciation to each associate at the end of the year to remind him that his contribution has not been forgotten. The certificate might be a printed document, suitable for display in the office or home of the donor. If the certificate is delivered in a cardboard frame and protected by a transparent, plastic window, it is more likely to be displayed, and extra mileage will be gained from those who see it. Each year the certificate can be updated by mailing current donors a small official gold seal attesting to the fact that they have kept their record of consecutive giving intact.

ATTRACTING DONOR DOLLARS TO HOSPITAL PROJECTS

Although tax laws will be changed from time to time, there is no way of escaping the fact that the people with money will be the targets of the heaviest levies. This fact makes it worthwhile for the tax-free hospital to put considerable effort into developing programs that will be of mutual benefit to them and to persons burdened with heavy tax loads.

Under certain circumstances, donors in high tax brackets can actually make money by giving it away, because tax shelters have been built into the law to provide for charitable giving. Although these shelters may be changed as tax laws are revised, it is most unlikely that the American people will permit any radical departure from tax-deductible giving that will undermine the voluntary, nonprofit community-service concept.

Under current laws, tax-deductible gifts may take several forms.

A donor, for example, can make a gift of securities and receive credit for the full current market value of the asset and save paying a heavy capital-gains tax on any substantial appreciation in its value. Or, if the donor would like to retain the original capital invested in his securities, he may sell the stock to a charity at his original purchase price, thus allowing the nonprofit corporation to own the stock at its appreciated value and permitting the donor to receive a tax deduction for the appreciated amount.

Another form of giving, which has grown widely in favor, is to contribute the asset but retain the income that it produces. Or, as a variation, the donor can contribute an asset, such as corporate securities, with the arrangement that the charity convert this into tax-exempt bonds, so that the donor can retain a lifetime income from the gift, free of both capital gains and income tax. Each gift of this nature would, of course, have to be carefully explored by competent tax authorities to make certain that all regulations are met. In this way, the donor can be given complete assurance that the contribution will stand undisturbed by tax agencies.

Chapter XV

LONG RANGE PLANNING

"LIFE" within the hospital organization often appears to move from one crisis to another. Perhaps this is related to the fact that saving lives frequently requires the peak effort of many people to meet effectively the patient's requirements during an emergency.

It is truly one of the wonders of the world to see hospital people go into emergency action without a moment's notice to save a life. Time and again I've seen a group of doctors, nurses and technicians who perhaps never have worked together before function as a smoothly coordinated team making every single action count as they fight for each precious breath.

In my mind I carry a vivid picture of six doctors and at least as many nurses and technicians working desperately in the emergency room to pull a beautiful little 6-year-old girl through a crisis. And I mean work! They weren't standing around wringing their hands. Somehow each one found his or her assignment. There were "cutdowns," transfusions, medications, cardiac massage. The little girl was rushed in, her life dangling by a thread, and within seconds the word went through the house. Doctors and nurses popped out of elevators and stairhalls converging silently and rapidly upon the emergency room. Coats were shed on the way, sleeves rolled up. An hour later, a life saved, all went back to their normal tasks.

AVOIDABLE CRISES

Medical emergencies cannot be eliminated—they are part of hospital life. But this is no execuse for tolerating other avoidable crises that can be eliminated by adequate planning. How many hospitals have a long-range plan? A clear conception of where they are going in five, ten, fifteen or twenty years?

It long has been known that lack of planning will result in drifting, embarking upon a course only to double back later when circumstances change. Or, what's worse, doing so when circumstances only *seem* to change. Just as accurate planning enables scientists to launch a manned space vehicle to intercept the moon, so planning will enable the hospital to anticipate effectively its needs years before they materialize.

Landscape architects can make important contributions to the appearance of the building while being mindful of the need for low cost maintenance.

HOW TO PLAN

Hospitals need to plan if they are to exercise any degree of control over their future; if they are to continue to serve their communities most effectively; if they are not to become the victim of circumstances; and if they are to avoid wasting valuable resources. How does a hospital approach long-range planning? Of many methods I believe the following to be most effective. Organize an advance planning committee to include capable representatives from the board, medical staff and management. Appoint a secretary and keep minutes. Begin an informal study by inviting representatives from each medical staff department and section to meet with the committee submitting a list of "dreams" the surgeons, for example, might have. Repeat not only until each section of the medical staff, but also board and management have had an opportunity to spell out their hopes.

Meanwhile, the literature should be searched to ascertain areas of services not presently covered. Seek to identify trends which seem to indicate decreasing need for one type of facility while others might be coming into focus.

This can develop into a very stimulating and enjoyable function. Experience proves the entire organization will benefit from a comprehensive search for new ideas and the opportunity to suggest a course of action. Depending upon the hospital, some allowance should be made for the organization to become oriented to the fact that suggestions for new equipment, procedures and services are being sought actively and not discouraged or rejected.

Recording and distributing the thoughts received in the form of minutes will accomplish a great deal as ideas need first to be on paper if they are to receive careful consideration from many people. One person's suggestions never will go far unless recorded for the benefit of others. Every building and piece of equipment, at its beginning stage, has been little more than words and sketches on paper.

As the ideas begin to accumulate, the problem will be to classify, think through and to establish a priority sequence for accomplishments. At this point those thoughts that have had the benefit of clear thinking and adequate expression in terms of the "who, what, when, where, why and how" will move to the forefront.

Many classifications will be possible. However, it may be helpful to sort ideas into the following categories:
1. Acceptable.
    a. No funds required
    b. Funds needed but project is financially self liquidating.
    c. Funds needed and adequate resources available.
    d. Costly with no funds available, nor income or other financial support in view.

2. Not acceptable.

Now the master "plan" begins to shape up. The near term will likely see the institution of recommendations which were accepted and offer no financial burden. Next there may be the ideas which involve an outlay of funds but where capital is available, or where the project will be self-liquidating. Those requiring an investment in funds with no return may fall into the long term. However, an idea in the middle or long-term category may be so important that it will take precedence.

TIMING, STRATEGY, TACTICS

Assuming we have a "master plan" in terms of objectives we need to give the most careful consideration to timing, strategy and tactics, all to include alternate approaches should the basic method fail. A time schedule should be established and used to check progress throughout the life of the plan. Periodic and realistic evaluation should take place. Additions and deletions should be made, based upon new information as it is presented.

Progress will be more rapid if the long-range plan is known throughout the organization. Aids such as three-dimensional drawings in color, or scale models, will assist people in visualizing various aspects of the plan. This, in turn, will expedite acceptance and help in obtaining necessary financial support.

Such a plan will improve significantly the overall effectiveness of the organization by minimizing wasted effort and in serving as a constant challenge. As the objectives are attained, a well-earned feeling of accomplishment will spread throughout all participating groups, serving as further stimulus not only for completion of the master plan, but to the daily and more mundane chores as well.

Planners will find another reward as individuals and groups step forward with the funds necessary to initiate and carry out some or all of the projects which would otherwise be delayed for lack of resources.

Excerpts of a formalized planning procedure developed by the Hospital Planning Association of Southern California will be found in the Appendix on page 95.

Chapter XVI

TOMORROW'S HOSPITAL

W ILL it be a ciricle, a square, a rectangle, an ellipse, or perhaps a combination of one or more forms?

Will patient rooms be pie-shaped?

Will patients' beds be in tandem, parallel, or opposite one another?

In tomorrow's hospital, will closed circuit television be combined with electronic monitoring to reduce the need for skilled nurses and technicians? What will be the function of electronic data processing?

Interesting as these design questions are, thought must first be given to the scope, quality, and the economics of the services that tomorrow's hospital will provide. Attention should also be focused on personnel, philanthropy, and planning.

First, the future general hospital will offer a full spectrum of diagnostic and therapeutic measures. It will be an educational health center actively engaged in training health workers and in helping people to better understand the importance of protecting health—their greatest single asset.

Second, in addition to medicine, surgery, obstetrics-gynecology, pediatrics, emergency, x-ray, laboratory and pharmacy, tomorrow's hospital will have definite arrangements to provide the patient with psychiatric attention, intensive care, limited care, rehabilitation programs, and the latest findings in medical research. It will keep abreast of all new developments, helping the doctors make a more accurate diagnosis and attain for the patient a more complete and rapid recovery.

Third, paper work will be virtually eliminated by the "systems approach."- From the moment the physician dictates his order until the patient's treatment is automatically recorded on tape, electronic equipment will be saving time, effort, money, improving accuracy, and reducing errors—all in the best interest of the patient.

Fourth, wasteful, unnecessary duplication of hospital facilities will be vastly curtailed. Effective long-range planning will become the order of the day.

Fifth, hospital support will come from a well-informed public whose members have been guided toward a realistic personal appreciation of the value of their hospital through organized effective efforts of the institution.

Sixth, the acute nursing shortage will decrease through planned effort to recruit nurses and toward making nursing careers attractive. Concentration of highly skilled people will permit more effective personnel utilization and will stimulate development of larger nursing units.

Seventh, hospital gift decisions will be made by highly sophisticated minds determined to see each dollar return its maximum value. Corporation and foundation executives will carefully weigh the advantages and disadvantages of contributions to large versus small operating units. Top-level executive thinking, objective and unemotional when allocation of corporate dollars is under review will channel donor dollars to the larger, well-known institutions.

Eighth, high standards requiring self-discipline by medical staffs will be expressed in the form of organized review committees: credential, tissue, medical and surgical audit, clinical pathological conference, medical records, joint conference, death review, and departmental. The medical staff will assume greater responsibility for "quality control" in medical practice. (If marginal practitioners are not curbed by their colleagues in larger measure, government will assume this responsibility.)

Ninth, a top quality governing body headed by a chairman of the board will include physicians and administrators to facilitate operating effectiveness and reduce problems in communication. Second-class directors and management will not be tolerated. Tomorrow's hospitals will be administered by highly trained individuals, perhaps designated as president or executive vice president, following the pattern of college, university, and industrial management.

Institutions will compete for top-rated, talented executives. Sought out will be the administrators who constantly test modern management practice in an effort to improve the quality of hospital service, meanwhile, continually searching for savings in the cost of operation.

Tenth, because of economic factors, the trend will be toward fewer and larger hospitals. In terms of present-day economy, a large hospital is still a small economic entity. A few large hospitals operate in the realm of a fifteen to twenty million dollar budget —small, in comparison with many other major business operations. Bigness *per se* is not all plus value, but unless an organization is of a certain size, it is denied many operating ingredients essential to maximum economy in operation. To illustrate: the large hospital can completely process linen for three cents a pound —half the linen-processing cost for the smaller hospital. Only a large laundry can effectively utilize expensive automated equipment and employ top quality supervision. This situation holds true for many other phases of hospital operation.

HOSPITALS IN TRANSITION

The future change in hospitals will not be unlike that which occurred in another segment of our economy—food marketing. It is realistic to say that the day of the corner grocery store is over. The small family business was unable to survive in the face of fundamental changes in the production, marketing and distribution of food. And with the disappearance of the small corner grocery store came great innovations in food marketing and major reductions in cost—often obscured by inflation and other factors. Although many miss the convenience of the corner grocery store, few would willingly give up the advantages of the supermarket.

Hospital care is in a comparable transition. Across the nation, small hospitals are merging to gain the advantage of a larger-scale operation. Small hospitals are growing internally to become larger units. Larger urban hospitals are developing satellite suburban units.

Transportation has permitted this changing pattern to emerge in response to heavy pressure from medical science—another major influence. A twenty-five-bed hospital may cost in the neighborhood of $250,000 to build. But one image amplification cineradiographic diagnostic machine, for example, cannot be obtained for less than $70,000. Even if it made economic sense to install a unit of this caliber in the small hospital, it is doubtful whether a radiologist would be available to interpret the film. Thus hospitals are being forced into larger units. This is the most significant development in today's hospital picture.

The American public is alert and sensitive, particularly to its health and its pocketbook. Americans will not sit on the sidelines and permit hospitals to waste their funds, or to deny them the best of care. For this reason I have not focused on the physical plant, or the configuration of the rooms, and other interesting questions. For unless hospitals do a better job of controlling costs and providing more complete hospital services, they will not be directly concerned with those interesting matters.

Facilities for programmed rehabilitation of patients are becoming more common.

To summarize, tomorrow's hospitals will be training centers; they will be larger; patients will have access to more diagnostic and therapeutic services; there will be far less unnecessary duplication of facilities; medical quality control will be more effective; top-quality directors and administrators will utilize all known management concepts to reduce costs; long-range planning will be utilized, and donor dollars will flow toward the larger, efficiently operated institutions.

APPENDIX

EXCERPTS FROM "GUIDELINES FOR INDIVIDUAL HEALTH FACILITY LONGRANGE PLANNING"*

GENERAL TRENDS WHICH AFFECT COMMUNITY NEEDS

Prediction of future needs for health service requires thorough knowledge and analysis of known facts, e.g., volume and types of services which have been provided, and trends in the characteristics of the population to be served, such as income levels, age composition, and total population change. Of equal if not greater importance in prediction of future needs are certain "imponderables" which are not amenable to accurate measurement. These imponderables may be broadly designated as trends in medical knowledge, organization and methods of financing. A few are mentioned in the following paragraphs. They are phrased as questions.

What changes may be expected in community attitudes toward the use of hospitals and other facilities?

Will the physicians organize themselves into utilization committees to assist individual physicians and health facilities in providing the best possible care to the patient?

Will there be a greater trend in the future toward the concentration of health services in health facilities for inpatient and outpatient diagnosis and treatment? For example, will hospitals be the setting for more outpatient care, health, examinations and preventive services?

Will the number of hospitals offering intern and resident training programs increase or decrease? What effect will such changes have upon the quality and financing of house staff services at hospitals?

* Prepared by the Hospital Planning Associaiton of Southern California, 1515 North Vermont Avenue, Los Angeles, California 90027. Based upon "Guide and Suggested Procedures" prepared by the Hospital Review and Planning Council of Southern New York, Inc.

To what extent will tax-supported health services increase in volume and variety, and be extended to economic groups not now being served?

Will this be accomplished through purchase of services from private institutions and professional personnel, or by direct provision through government employees and institutions?

Will voluntary health insurance expand horizontally to protect additional segments of the population, and vertically to provide more comprehensive health service benefits? If so, will such expansion involve supplementation of subscriber payments with tax monies to assure coverage for low-income and hard-to-enroll individuals? Will such a development tend to change the pattern of utilization of health insurance benefits; e.g., will outpatient care be provided through such programs?

Will there be a continuation, or even acceleration, of present trends in hospital use, such as: length of stay, progressive patient care, home care program, use of nursing homes, etc.?

Will the concentration of certain categories of specialized diagnostic and therapeutic facilities and professional personnel in hospital settings increase or decrease, and will this trend alter referral patterns among private medical practitioners?

Will institutional care of long-term illness be provided primarily in nursing homes or in specialized units of general hospitals?

Will medical practitioners be encouraged to utilize hospital settings for preventive and rehabilitative services, and will such services become generally available for both inpatients and outpatients?

To what degree, and by what methods, will hospitals coordinate their programs through joint use of facilities or by cooperative agreements with other health agencies?

Consideration of these questions is an important preliminary to institutional long-range planning for professional and economic development and administration. Many of these factors may not be determined quantitatively, but it is important to recognize and consider their possible effects upon community needs and an individual institution's role in meeting them.

COMMITTEE ORGANIZATION AND OPERATION FOR INDIVIDUAL HEALTH FACILITIES

The responsibilities of a long-range planning committee are sufficiently broad and time consuming to warrant its status as a separate and permanent group that is responsible directly to the board of trustees. It is inadvisable to add the planning function to the work of an existing committee concerned with finance, medical affairs, construction or public relations.

Composition and General Functions

Each institution will undoubtedly designate membership in accord with its special situation, but it seems important to include adequate representation from the board of trustees, the medical staff and the administration. The chairmanship should be held by a trustee, preferably by the president.

It is important that financial, organizational, and architectural advice be sought early in the deliberations of the committee. Likewise the committee should inform itself of the programs of official and voluntary agencies. Since the medical staff will perform or supervise all professional care, they must be consulted on all phases of the functional program.

Membership of the committee should be large enough to include varying opinions on the hospital's future, but small enough to function effectively. The terms of office should be long enough to provide continuity in fact-finding and to insure the development of recommendations for action.

The committee's task is to develop agreement on the long-range program, based upon its concept of the hospital's role in the community. If the long-range plan involves expansion, the functional program should then be translated into architectural terms indicating the space needs for equipment and personnel, and appropriate design to achieve efficient operation. The final consideration is an estimate of the capital expenditures which will be required, and the sources from which necessary funds may be obtained for construction and for operating expenses.

PLANNING PROCEDURES

Planning involves time, effort, understanding and courage. Professional advice and services are important in all stages of the process — collection of data, analysis of administrative procedures, estimates of cost and revenue, and proposals for layout and design of building. Proper attention to the several aspects of long-range planning and development will require functioning subcommittees. In any case, the committee's responsibilities would justify employment or assignment of professional staff to work with and for the committee. The following steps are phases of long-range planning by an institution.

1. Establishment of Hospital's Long-range Mission or Objective

The Committee should delineate clearly an ideal role for the hospital, and outline the functions which it will perform in the provision of health care for the community. The functional program should be expressed in writing as the basis for discussion and revision from time to time. Will the hospital essentially serve the neighboring residents, or will it emphasize the care of patients referred from a much wider geographic area? Will it provide the setting for programs of health service research and education? Will it attempt to provide all types of professional equipment and services? Will it accept and serve all economic, radial, and ethnic groups in the population? Might the mission be accomplished more effectively by moving to a new site or by affiliation with another institution? Does the present medical staff endorse the committee's concept of the hospital's long-range mission? Will the new activities require substantial additions to the present medical and paramedical attending staff? Have the professional personnel to be engaged in these activities expressed interest in affiliating with the institution?

2. Appraisal of the Institution's Present Role in Meeting Community Needs

It is important to be realistic when analyzing the hospital's professional personnel, services and facilities. What are the strong and weak points in the present functional program? Standards of professional service are determined by the qualifications of the medical staff who perform or supervise the patient care at the hospital. Does the present attending medical staff need to be augmented by house or institutional staffs? How many full-time and part-time physicians are required; for what purposes? Is there an adequate number of certified practitioners in the various medical specialties and subspecialties? Are younger well-trained physicians being added to the attending staff? Are they demonstrating their loyalty by participating in the service to non-paying patients? What teaching affiliations are desirable or obtainable? Have emergency care and social services been developed? Are there adequate outpatient services and facilities for the care of the chronically ill? From what geographic areas does the hospital draw its inpatients and outpatients, and in what proportions? Which medical staff members use this facility as the hospital of first choice? Have adjacent hospitals increased their facilities and services in recent years? Have new ones been established? What cooperative arrangements have been developed with other institutions, e.g., nursing education, and other educational programs, planning, continuity of care, purchasing?

3. *Consideration of Problems in Achieving the Long-range Functional Program*

A community's health needs will change in volume and character during a generation. This makes it essential to appraise present trends in the population, medical practice government health care programs, economic development, community attitudes, and hospital administration. What basic changes in the hospital's present functional program are contemplated? Will it draw patients from a broader or more restricted health-service area? Will the new program require more beds for patients? Will the program stress the idea of progressive patient care; preventive services; rehabilitation; physician's private examining rooms; increased emergency and outpatient services; residency programs; health examination programs; point use of specialized facilities with other institutions? Is there evidence of general approval by the medical profession and general public of the revised long-range functional programs?

4. *Establishment of Short-term Priorities*

New health facilities and services cost money, which may not be immediately available. Some phases of the long-range program must be given priority sequence and first claim on available financial resources. Such decisions involve agreement among the attending medical and dental staff, the administration, architectural advisors and possible financial contributors. They should be consistent with the long-range goals of the institution. When time-priority is given to capital investment for new construction, many questions arise. Have special space utilization studies been made which justify the need for immediate action? Does the medical staff concur with the committee's priorities? Have alternative measures been considered to deal with immediate needs, such as increased use of outpatient diagnostic services prior to admission, seven-day-a-week, round-the-clock availability of supporting services, establishment of utilization committee to review hospital stays, etc.?

5. *Planning for Specific Services*

A functional program must be planned in detail if it is to achieve high standards at reasonable cost. This may require special administrative and engineering studies of current practices. What changes are predicted in the immediate and long-run work load and space requirements for specific health services, e.g., beds for medicine, surgery, obstetrics, and pediatrics; outpatient care; emergency care; social service; pharmacy; employee health programs; dentistry; hospital based home care; hospitalization of long-term cases, etc?

What will be the immediate and long-range effects on space needs and personnel for the adequate administration of such functions as accounting, purchasing, storage, maintenance, records, dietary service, medical records; Do the functional programs take into account the requirements of related activities, such as research, education, in-service training, auxiliaries, preventive care, meetings, religious observance and employee housing?

6. *Organization and Staffing for the Future*

Has the hospital developed uniform personnel policies and an organizational pattern with clear definition of authority and responsibility? Are any specific changes obviously desirable? Will the new program require realignment or regrouping of certain administrative functions? Is there reasonable assurance of an adequate supply of professional and lay personnel to staff the new or expanded activities? Will the patient care program involve greater use of auxiliary personnel, such as floor clerks and nurses aides? Is there present idle space or personnel who might be made available during "peak" activities elsewhere?

7. *Estimating Financial and Construction Requirements*

Construction is the final phase of long-range planning and development. Capital planning will be effective only if it follows careful functional planning. The written functional program becomes the basis for a written architectural program, which is the designation of space needs for facilities and personnel required to accomplish the long-range mission and objectives of the institution. Physicians, administrators, trustees, and architects should combine their professional knowledge and experience to assure that future investment in plant and equipment will contribute to efficient service and professional standards.

During each phase of the planning process, the public should be informed of the possibility that additional capital funds may be required to implement the immediate and long-range programs. The community should know why the hospital proposes to modify its service program, and why capital expenditures are required for expansion, replacement, or modernization. Capital expenditures affect total operating expenses. Large-scale purchasers of health care—such as government and prepayment agencies—should be assured that the long-range program has been developed in accord with total community needs, and will not result in excessive costs of operation.

Estimates must be made of the relative role of government, philanthropy, and operating income in financing the capital expenditures. Government agencies now play an important role in the financing of health facilities — general hospitals, nursing homes, preventive services, outpatient care, etc. Tax monies have also been widely used for purchase of health services from private institutions and professional persons. The amounts involved in providing health facilities are so great that philanthropy can carry only a small portion of the load. Corporations and foundations may be expected to allocate their contributions in accord with advice that a specific program is part of a community-wide plan for health service.

Consideration must be given to the rapidly increasing annual budgetary costs. New and improved services entail further budgetary demands. There should be a careful appraisal of the effect of expanding facilities or services on the institution's annual operating costs. Government, third party payors, business, labor and the public are all becoming perturbed at the rapidly increasing costs. New sources of annual maintenance support must be developed which are acceptable to the public in the roles of policyholder and taxpayer.

Information for Committee Study and Appraisal

The procedure previously outlined have been stated in terms of various questions which must be answered by an institution's long-range planning and development committee. Intelligent replies are dependent on the analysis of important facts which must be brought to the attention of the committee.

The facts may be broadly classified as (a) information about the hospital — its history, resources and present program; (b) information about the community — its population growth and composition, total health needs, available health resources, and various factors influencing the demand or need for hospitalization.

Information About the Hospital

Information about the institution will usually be obtainable from the statistical, financial and professional records and reports maintained by the hospital. In some instances special studies or analyses will be required to develop comparisons and relationships among different phases of the program, or to reveal trends during a period of time.

The following types of data ordinarily will be available from a hospital's current accounting, statistical and medical records. The tabulations will require some special analysis, but they represent information which is essential to long-range planning and development. These facts should be tabulated for comparison of facilities or services over several annual periods, e.g., 1950, 1955, 1960, 1962, 1964, with projection, if applicable, for the next decade.

Bed Complement (or capacity)
Medical, surgical obstetrical, pediatrics, long-term care, psyciatric, other.
Types of room accommodations.

Services
Patient days, admissions, newborn days and births, all classified by professional service and type of accommodation.

Outpatients, and Visits Classified

Specific Professional Services
Surgical operations, obstetrical deliveries, radiography, radiotherapy, pathology, physiotherapy, social service, etc.

Operating Expenditures
Object classification: Salaries and wages, supplies and materials, purchased services, interest expense, depreciation, other.
Departmental classification.

Annual Income
Classified by general sources: Individual patients, nonprofit and commercial insurance, government payments, endowment, contributions, other.
Classified by revenue-producing departments.

Annual Capital Expenditures

Classified by sources of funds—philanthropic contributions, government grants, commercial loans, net earnings, other.

Analysis of Medical Staff

Special certification, age distribution, number of annual inpatient admissions per doctor, duration of membership, other staff appointments.

Analysis of Geographic Residence of Inpatients and Outpatients

Limitations of Present Program

Types of patients not accepted, e.g., obstetric, psychiatric, narcotic.

Types of services not provided, e.g., radiotherapy, home care, heart surgery.

Present Cooperative or Contractual Arrangements

For joint use of facilities or provision of services, e.g., cobalt unit, special surgery, laundry, maintenance, dietary, etc.

Detailed Analysis of existing Plant and Equipment

In terms of safety, efficiency, adequacy and suitability for present and future programs.

Other Information Sources

Population Information

1. State Department of Finance.
2. Bureau of Hospitals (California State Plan).
3. Respective County and City Planning Departments.
4. Security First National Bank (Research Department, Los Angeles).
5. Selected Utility Companies.
6. U. S. Bureau of the Census.
7. Los Angeles Chamber of Commerce (for comparative purposes primarily).
8. Los Angeles Regional Transportation Study (LARTS).
9. Welfare Planning Councils.
10. California Taxpayers Association.

Health Facilities Information

1. Hospital Planning Association of Southern California.
2. Individual Health Facilities.

  3. Bureau of Hospitals, State Department of Public Health.
  4. Bureau of Private Institutions, State Department of Mental Health.
  5. California Hospital Association.
  6. California Association of Nursing Homes, etc.
  7. Los Angeles County Nursing Home Association.
  8. Hospital Council of Southern California.
  9. United Hospital Association.
 10. American Hospital Association (Guide Issue of Hospitals —data is incomplete).
 11. Joint Commission on Accreditation of Hospitals.
 12. California Commission on Accreditation of Nursing Homes.
 13. Department of Social Welfare.

Medical Practice Information
  1. California Medical Association.
  2. American Medical Association.
  3. County Medical Societies and Associations.
  4. Medical Staff Roster of Individual Health Facilities.
  5. Los Angeles County Civil Defense Authority.
  6. California Board of Medical Examiners.
  7. Speciality and Professional Directories.

INDEX

B

Bank finance mortgage loans
  considerations studied by bank, 77
  factoresto consider, 77
  requirements by bank, 77
Bed, all electric, advantages, 28
Brown, Ray E., vi
Bugbee, George, xii

C

Classifications hospitals
  convalescent, 15-16
  general, 14
    advanced services, 14
    objective, 14
    usual services, 14
  nursing homes, 15-16
  ownership, 11-14
    community or proprietary, *See*
      Proprietary hospitals
    nonprofit, 11-13, *See also* Non-
      profit hospitals
    voluntary, 11
  size, 14
  specialized, 14
    children's, 114
    for long-term illnesses, 14
  teaching, 15
    affiliation with university medical
      schools, 15
    number of, 15
    training programs in, 15
Community hospital, *See* Proprietary
  hospital
Convalescent homes and nursing homes,
  14-15
  chain-operated, 14-15
  Federal standards, 15
  importance added due to medicare, 14
  increased costs, 15
  level of care, 14
  ownership, 14
  range of care, 14
  size and economics, 15
Curry, W. D. "Bob", 73

D

Dedication of hospital, 67-68
  commemorative brochure prepared, 68
  follow-up news stories, 68
  planning one year prior to, 67-68
  previews for special groups, 68
  purpose, 68-69
  radio and TV interviews, 68
  schedule for, 68
  special groups invitations, 68
  special tours, 68
  use special edition local paper, 68
DeWitt, Harry, 76

E

Equipment, 51-54
  based on building design, 53-54
  examination major items by displays,
    51-52
  guides for vertical transportation, 54
  preparation realistic equipment
    budget, 53
  problem eager sales representatives, 54
  requesting suggestions and opinions
    from experienced staff, 52-53
  role competent purchasing staff, 51
  unit turnkey plan with hospital
    supplier, 51
  use bid basis by manufacturers and
    distributors, 51
  use U.S. Public Health Service lists, 53

F

Financing
  bank finance mortgage loans, 76
  capital needs for general hospital by
    population, table, 70
  hospital bond issues, 75, *See also*
    Hospital bond issues
  insurance company mortgage loans,
    77-78
  investment needed per person in
    community, 70
  for general hospital, 70

for mental or long-term hospitals, 70
lease purchasing, 76
long-term, low-pressure, fund de-
    velopment, *See* Long-term fund
    development
mortgage loan underwriters, 78-79
role good hospital management in, 5-6
sources, 71-73
    common, 71
    relation size to, 73
    survey of ones used recently, table 72
    use community fund drives, 73
    use Hill-Harris funds, 73
    use of experts to locate, 73
    use of more than one, 71
voluntary fund drives, 73-74. *See also*
    Voluntary fund drives
Franklin, Benjamin, 11
Frishman, Harry, 75

G

Governing boards
    director of, 17
    in government hospitals, 22
    in proprietary hospitals, 22
    in Roman Catholic hospitals, 22
    of nonprofit hospitals, 12-13
    of voluntary hospitals, 11

H

Hill-Harris funds, uses of, table, 72
Hospital administrator, graduate
    programs in, 5-6
Hospital bond issues, 75
    basic guide lines for success, 75
    importance proper planning, 75
    need appeal to emotions of citizens,
        75
    negative issues anticipated, 75
Hospital functioning, 17-22
    checks and balances, 18-22
        concept in practice, 20
        delegation authority and respon-
            sibility to achieve objective, 21
        need for good communications,
            20-21
        of doctors, 19
        participation medical staff, board
            and management, 21
        possibilities imbalance, 18

results out of balance management,
    18-19
role chief executive to resist policy-
    forming groups, 21
role executive officer, 21
roles doctors play, 19
roles hospital trustees, 20
shifts in leadership, 20
teamwork as essential, 18
use "three-headed" organizaiton, 19
common goal, 17-18
essential elements, 17
    employee groups, 17
    governing boards, 17
    medical staff, 17
    volunteer workers, 17

I

Insurance company mortgage loans,
    77-78
    major factors considered, 77-78
    terms of, 78
Intensive-care units, advantages, 29
Intercom, electric, advantages, 28
Interior design, 33-39
    Appeal to the eye and mind, 33
    assignment check list, 38-39
    factors in assessing professional
        designs, 36-37
    feeling of reassurance needed in, 33
    fundamental function, 38
    "functionalism" not same as, 34
    goals, 33, 39
    guide to selection, 36-38
        development of guides, 37
        early retaining of designer, 37-38
        factors in assessing design firms,
            36-37
        use of scale drawings and samples,
            37
        use team concept in planning with
            architects, engineers, designer, 38
    interior and exterior excellence, 39
    landscape architect, 39
    obtaining professional advice, 36-37
        economic value of, 34
        for cabinet details, 34-35
        for lighting, 34
        for mill work, 34
        for planning, 34
        for public rooms planning, 35

for selection materials, fabrics and
wall coverings, 35
for use interior pace, 34
from decorators, 35
from manufactures and distributors,
35
from merchandising firms, 35
personal inspection previous work
done by, 36
professional interior designer or
design firm, 36
payment to designer, 39

K

Kenny, D. J., 78

L

Landscape architect, 39
illustration work of, 87
Lease purchasing, 76
evaluating advantages and
disadvantages, 76
factors inherent in, 76
Long term fund development, 7, 80-85
advantages, 7
an associates group, 82-84
annual membership dues, 82-83
effectiveness of, 83
methods used to establish, 82-83
presentation certificate of appreciation to members, 84
programs for meetings, 83-84
progress reports to, 83
use of at public ceremonies, 84
attracting donor dollars to hospital
projects, 84-85
contribution asset, retention income,
85
forms tax-deductible gifts, 84-85
use tax shelters for, 84
gifts from other agencies, 81-82
appeal for assistance on small
projects, 82
appeals to service-oriented groups,
82
follow-up after receipt of a gift, 82
progress reports, 82
use key leadership of, 82
presenting proposal in concise and
careful manner, 80

request in form report, 80
setting definite dollar amount
required, 80
tailoring appeals to various types
potential donors, 80
use simple, clear-cut, direct mail
appeal, 80-81
contents, 81
elements in, 81
letter of thanks to donor, 81
repeat gifts, 81
Long-range planning, 86-89
advance planning committee, 87-89
ascertaining areas of services not
covered, 88
categories of ideas, 88
identification trends, 88
organization, 87-88
recording and distributing minutes
planning committee, 88
study hopes and dreams of staff, 88
avoidable crises, 86-87
committee organization and operation
for individual health facilities, 97
composition, 97
general functions, 97
individual health facilities, 97
size of committee, 97
task of committee, 97
general trends which affect
community needs, 95-96
how to plan, 87-89
information about hospital, 103-104
analysis of geographic residence
of patients, 104
analysis of medical staff, 104
annual capital expenditures, 104
annual income, 103
bed complement, 103
detailed analysis existing plant
and equipment, 104
limitations present program, 104
operating expenditures, 103
outpatients and visits classified, 103
present cooperative or contractual
arrangements, 104
services, 103
informaiton for committee study and
appraisal, 102
information sources, 104-105
health facilities information, 104-105
medical practice information, 105

population information, 104
planning procedures, 98-102
    appraisal of present role in meeting
        community needs, 98-99
    consideration problems in achieving
        functional program, 99-100
    establishment mission or objective,
        98
    establishment of short-term
        priorities, 100
    estimating financial and con-
        struction requirements, 101-102
    organization and staffing for
        future, 101
    planning for specific services,
        100-101
timing, strategy, tactics, 89

M

Money-saving tips, 40-46
    allowance adequate time for bidding,
        40
    allowance latitude for color paint,
        floor covering, etc., 42
    avoiding construction change orders,
        42
    cross-checking plans and
        specifications, 41-42
    early use outside resource people,
        41
    exploration methods of financing, 42
    filing updated plans and specifications
        for later uses, 43
    involvement opinion leaders to avoid
        undue criticism, 43
    onesite supervisor hired by hospital,
        42
    penalty clause for delayed completion
        construction, 40-41
    planned tours by staff during
        construction, 43
    planning parking areas, 41
    pre-acceptance schedule, 42
    setting of bid-closing time, 40
    timing of bidding and construction,
        40
    use comprehensive checklist, 44
        example, 44-46
    use full-size model patient use for
        evaluations, 42-43

use Polaroid photos pipe and
    conduit, 43
Mortgage loan underwriters, 78-79
    factors in, 79
    normal costs, 79
    requirements for, 78
    standard terms of mortgage, 79

N

Needs, 3-10
    adequate electrical wiring, 3
    adequate parking facilities, 3
    answers
        adequate capital, 5
        competent hospital management, 5-6
        cooperation area hospitals, 9
        higher percentage bed occupancy,
            6-7
        long-term, low-pressure, fund-
            development, 7
        lower patient cost and better
            patient care, 6
        role hospital management, 10
        role medical staff, 10
        role trustees, 10
        summary, 9-10
        use of experts as consultants, 7-8
    coordinated building additions, 3
    expansion, 71
    full size patient rooms, 3
    labor saving equipment, 4
    modern equipment for diagnosis
        and treatment, 4
    modern toilet facilities, 4
    modernization, 71
    safe buildings, 4
    space for specialized departments, 4-5
    summary, 9-10
    well-designed department areas, 4-5
    well-designed nursing units, 4
Nonprofit hospitals, 11-13
    ability to shift funds readily, 12-13
    defined, 12
    explanation, 11
    government units, 13
    limitation on profit, 12
    privilege enjoyed, 12
    services possible only by, 12
    use of profits, 12

P

Parking areas, planning of, 41
Pitfalls in planning avoided, 47-50
  anticipation and preparation for
    future needs, 48
  centralization some facilities, 49
  development specialized service and
    cooperation other hospitals, 49
  establishment definite schedule, 50
  expansion or remodeling versus new
    structure, 48-49
  expression total concept in writing,
    50
  need define objectives and evaluate
    requests and ideas, 47-48
  need to think big, 47
  use checklist, 50
  use old building for various purposes,
    49
  use professional interior designer, 47
Planning and expansion team, 23-26
  building committee, 23-24
    advisors, 24
    management hospital representation,
      23-24
    medical staff representation, 23
    secretary, 24
    selection of, 23-24
  initiation of expansion, 23
    by executive officer, 23
    by inspecting officials, 23
    by physician, 23
  professional advisors, 24-26
    architects, 24
    engineers, 25-26
    hospital consultant, 24-25
Proprietary hospital, 13-14
  establishment by private capital, 13
  governing board, 22
  limitations, 13-14
  payment property and income taxes, 14
  percent of all beds in, 13
  percent of all hospitals represented
    by, 13
Public acceptance, 65-69
  dedication as major event, 67-69
  facts for general news media, 67
  financial support evolving from, 66
  golden opportunity, 65-66
  immediate hospital "family," 67
    giving news prior public, 67

  use internal newsheet, 67
  information in depth, 67-69
    for hospital "family," 67
    for public at large, 67-69
  need for, 65-66
  obtaining future patients by, 65-66
  public-education programs and, 65
  reports each forward step to public,
    66-67
  stepladder to success, 66-67

S

Staffing, 55-61
  medical staff, participation in
    planning new hospital, 59
  preopening personnel, 58
    chief executive officer, 58
    contracts for medical specialists, 58
    heads of major departments, 58
    purchasing agent, 58
  quality control, 56-61
    check sheet, example, 60-61
    measurement, 56
    overstaffing during initial phase
      operation unit, 57
    staffing patterns by departments, 57
    standard hours care per patient per
      day, 56-57
    standard hours care per patient per
      day, table, 57
    use of standards, 57
  standards, 55-56
    components of patient care, 56
    experience in California, 55-56
    nursing time per patient, 56

T

Telephone, bedside, advantages, 28
Test run, 62-64
  advantages, 62
  break-in period, 63
  clean-up, 62
  employee orientation, 63-64
  preparation meals for working crews,
    64
  processing new linen, 64
  receiving, inspecting, placing
    equipment, 62-63
    use armed security guards, 63
  use volunteers as patients for a
    day, 64

Tomorrow's hospital, 90-94
  administration, 91-92
  basis financial gifts to, 91
  care offered, 90
  decreased nursing shortage, 91
  elimination paper work, 90-91
  facilities for programmed
    rehabilitation, photograph, 93
  governing body, 91
  hospitals in transition, 92-93
  lack duplication, 91
  preventive health, 90
  scope of, 90
  standards self imposed by staff, 91
  summary, 94
  support of, 91
  trend toward fewer and larger
    hospitals, 92
Total design factors, 27-32
  better facilities, 27-29
    adjacent bathroom accommodations,
      28
    advantages double-corridor
      design, 27-28
    advantages single-corridor design,
      27, 28
    avoiding extremes in design, 27
    bedside telephone, 28
    compromise in design, 27
    intensive-care units, 29
    lack conformity in design, 27
    mechanical features and conser-
      vation time of nurse, 28-29
    relation basic nursing unit size
      and number patients, 28
    use all-electric bed, 28
    use electronic intercom, 28
    use single and double-corridor
      design, 27
  future expansion, 32
    acquistion property for, 32
    oversizing key diagnostic, ther-
      apeutic and service departments,
      32
    provisions for, 32

  unification higher-lower operating
      costs, 29-31
    effectiveness lesser skilled persons
      in large unit, 30
    increased distance nursing station
      to remote bedside, 29
    need for longer hospital beds, 30
    need for time-saving devices, 30
    nursing unit management effec-
      tiveness and cost of care, 30
    over economical space allocation
      contraindicated, 30
    purpose increased nursing unit
      size, 29
    relation salaries to initial
      construction and equipment
      cost, 30
    room with electric beds, photograph,
      31
    size elevators, 31
    supporting services needed near
      nursing unit, 30
    upgrading quality supervision and
      management nursing personnel,
      29-30
    width for corridors, 31

V

Voluntary funds drives, 73-74
  factors basic to successful
    appropriate timing, 74
    competent hospital administrator, 74
    convincing evidence, 73
    dedicated and confidence inspiring,
      74
    medical staff democratically
      organized, 74
    must measure up, 73
    no other alternatives, 73
Voluntary hospitals
  founder of first one in United States,
    11
  governing board, 11
  religious, 11
Volunteer program, essence of, 17